THE TENACIOUS
MISSIONARY

How God gave a girl from a small town in New Mexico a purpose in life as a missionary to America

By

Christine Schulden

Christine Schulden

2021 © Mission Nation Publishing

ISBN: 978-0-9992577-8-4

A Word from the President of the Florida/Georgia Lutheran Women's Missionary League

Mission work has been a central theme for the Lutheran Women's Missionary League since it became an auxiliary of the Lutheran Church—Missouri Synod in 1942. In the last seventy-five years, the LWML has funded more than $100 million in mission grants to those in need.

Like the other thirty-nine districts in the LWML, the Florida-Georgia District has a heart for missions. We are committed to spreading the gospel of Christ to those here and abroad. We do this with the use of our mites (money) that fund our mission grants.

With grants to ministries such as Mission Nation, stories about what God has done for those who need him are shared. The "New Missionaries to America" grant is helping us see that the United States is a mission field as the country grows in diversity. What a wonderful gift it is that the Word is available to those in the United States who might not have been able to hear it in their own countries! People from different countries are coming to the United States not only for a better life, but because Jesus wants them to know the gospel of his love.

The Florida-Georgia LWML District is humbled to help those with needs of all kinds and to spread his grace and love to all we are blessed to serve.

Serving the Lord with gladness always …

Gayle Caruso, **President, Florida-Georgia LWML District**

Glossary of Spanish Terms

abuela: grandma

abuelo: grandpa

Dios mío: my God

diputado: representative

gracias: thank you

hija: daughter

La Telaraña de Charlotte: Charlotte's Web

lazo: rope

madre: mother

mercadito: small grocery store

mercado: market

mi'jita: my daughter

municipio: municipality

norteño: northern

Nuevo México: New Mexico

vaquero: cowboy

viejita: used affectionately by an elderly man to refer to one's elderly wife

Table of Contents

Prologue
Nuevo México | 1600s

The snarl of a bobcat crossed the plains, and Juan Pablo García's sheep bleated as they bumped into one another. The herding dogs, two rakish but focused guardians, growled and snapped at the sheep on the fringes, circling them with sharp yips and the occasional nip. Juan Pablo grasped the reins and put a hand on his long rifle.

A patch of scrub brush rustled to his left. The stock horse he was riding snorted but kept pace with the slow walk Juan Pablo wanted. He knew the horse could smell the fear rising from the flock and sense the agitation of the dogs. But since the horse was one of the ranch's best, Juan trusted him to remain calm.

The García family had left Spain years before and settled in what was known as *Nuevo México*. They'd paid good money to bring many of their prized sheep with them on their trek across the Atlantic so they would have wool and mutton to sell once they reached the new world. Life as a *vaquero*, or cowboy, was all Juan Pablo knew. His family had been sheep herders for generations, making their livelihood from breeding strong stock. But the topography was different here, the plains unable to protect the sheep like the mountains and valleys he'd been used to in their homeland. The daily threats of black bears, cougars, bobcats, and wolves were something he'd never get used to.

1

Juan Pablo wrapped the reins around the horn on the saddle and gently pressed his spurs against the horse's flanks. The *lazo* hooked to the saddle would do no good; catching a bobcat with a loop of rope was hopeless. Juan Pablo tapped his gun and prided himself for loading it before he'd left in the hazy dawn to take the sheep out to graze. He pulled the flintlock halfway and reached for the powder horn that hung from a leather cord around his neck. He shakily uncapped it and carefully poured gunpowder into the pan. With one hand, he recapped the powder horn and let it fall to his side. Yellow-green eyes gleamed from the scrub brush. Juan Pablo hoped the growling dogs, now foaming at the mouth, were ready for a fight. He wouldn't lose one of the family's precious sheep or lambs to a bobcat.

He sighted-in the rifle along the dense line of vegetation where he'd last seen movement. He'd have only one shot, so he had to make it count. Suddenly one of the smaller sheep escaped the flock and darted toward the scrub brush. In one motion, the bobcat cleared the height of the brush and leapt at the terrified sheep.

The bobcat and the sheep rolled together, kicking up clouds of dust. Juan Pablo squinted, spotting the snarling cat just as its claws sunk into the sheep's side, and pulled the trigger.

The dogs rushed the bobcat, their howls telling Juan Pablo the animal would no longer be a threat to him or to the flock. Juan Pablo dismounted and slapped the horse on the haunches to let him know he'd done a good job.

While the dogs tore at the bobcat, Juan Pablo knelt beside the injured sheep and pressed a hand into the thick wool to feel its heartbeat. The animal seemed more shocked than injured, and Juan Pablo thanked the Lord it was still alive. Even though his family tended hundreds of animals on their many acres near Santa Fe, he knew his father would have been distressed over the loss of even one small sheep.

Juan Pablo held the sheep gently in his lap. He stroked its velvet nose and patted its soft head. The dogs, jowls tinted red, sniffed at the fallen sheep, one giving a low whine.

"It's OK, Salty," Juan Pablo said, smiling at one of the concerned dogs. "This one is fine. He'll join the flock once he's gotten over his fear."

Salty lay next to Juan Pablo, putting his snout on his paws. The other herding dog, Pepper, tended to the flock, circling them together with low barks.

"It's not your fault, you know," Juan Pablo told the dog. "You'll see. All of the other sheep will welcome him back into the flock as if he'd never left."

The sheep stirred, stood on wobbly legs, and then meandered back to the fold. Salty watchfully trotted nearby.

Juan Pablo let out a sigh as he hoisted himself back into the saddle. He knew he was doing the right thing with his life. Sheep farming may not be his family's line of business forever; he couldn't predict what future generations would be called to do. But he loved taking care of the sheep that wandered off and leading them back to the fold.

Juan Pablo clicked his tongue and tapped the horse's flanks with his spurs. The dogs circled the flock once again, directing the sheep to follow Juan Pablo to a newer, fresher pasture—one where, no matter the danger, he would go to any length to keep them safe. Juan Pablo García was, if nothing else, tenacious. It was a quality his descendants would need to tame this wild land.

Chapter 1
Lumberton, New Mexico | 1966

With a threadbare white towel, Melissa wiped the already clean counter. Well weathered from years of use, its wood was engraved with thick lines much like the wrinkles on the faces of the bar's daily patrons. Melissa rubbed at a water mark that had been there for as long as she could remember, wondering how many people from the reservation had sat in that spot, retelling their life stories. How many of their fears and woes had been shared with the bartender, her grandfather?

"Thank you for helping, *mi'jita*." Her grandfather put the whiskey glass he'd been wiping dry in line with the others. Melissa couldn't help but notice the way the early evening's light coming in through the windows made rainbow prisms when it touched the glass.

Ten-year-old Melissa lived with her grandparents in Lumberton, New Mexico, near the Jicarilla Apache Reservation, with her younger brother, Mark. She spent her days at a Catholic school with other Spanish-speaking locals and the Apache children. Her school was small; there were only two classrooms, and grades one through twelve were taught together in English by a handful of kind nuns from Germany. Melissa always got her work done early and loved when she had the chance to help the younger children with their studies while the nuns taught other students. After she'd completed her homework, she would join her grandparents at the bar they owned and do little jobs that made their lives easier.

"You need to take care of that," Melissa's grandmother said firmly, entering the common bar area from the kitchen. Some said the bawdy laughter that seemed to precede Mr. Velarde could be heard for a mile, and Melissa agreed. She heard his loud voice first; then the door to the bar opened with its familiar groan and squeak. Melissa's grandmother wiped her hands on her apron, regarding her husband with a raised eyebrow and cock of her head.

"This week."

Melissa's grandmother gave her husband a direct stare. He grinned at her. "I promise, *Viejita*."

She threw up her hands. "Alejandro, I've been hearing that for at least a month now!"

With a wink at his granddaughter, Alejandro Mercure placed another immaculate glass next to the others and looked at Mr. Velarde expectantly. "The usual, my friend?" He plucked a bottle of an amber liquid from behind the bar.

Alejandro and Gregorita Mercure with an Apache friend from the reservation.

"Yes, sir!" The barstool scraped along the floor as Mr. Velarde pulled it from its spot and sat down. He was a formidable man, with a wide chest, huge forearms, and strong, broad shoulders. To Melissa he looked like a giant—a giant with a great sense of humor and the kindest eyes she'd ever seen.

Her grandfather expertly turned over one of the freshly washed tumblers and poured in a healthy amount of the liquid.

Mr. Velarde rotated his pointer finger, encouraging her grandfather to pour more.

"A double today?"

Mr. Velarde nodded. "Felled some trees today. Figure I earned it."

The timber industry was popular on the reservation, as were sheep ranching and oil and gas production. But there was still underlying animosity toward those who'd converted parts of the reservation into industry rather than leaving it to their tribe to maintain.

Back in the late 1800s, when the United States government awarded the Apache tribes in New Mexico and Colorado their reservations, the land was inferior to what had been taken from them. It wasn't rich agriculturally, and it did not include access to places the Apache held sacred. Although the United States government allowed the reservations to self-govern and provided stipends for each tribe member, the relationship between the Apache people and the government was irreparably strained. The Apache did not want to support United States industries; they believed that whatever was on reservation property belonged to them and that the tribe should be the sole benefactor of the financial windfall the land provided.

"You hungry?" Melissa's grandmother regarded Mr. Velarde after he'd downed his double. "I have tortillas ready. Some beans and rice made."

Mr. Velarde rubbed his round belly. "I only have this because of your beans and rice, Mrs. Mercure. Once I start eating your cooking, I can't stop." He looked over at Melissa. "That might be why you've grown so tall. Your *abuela* feeds you such good, healthy food."

"Is Julian coming today?" Part of the reason Melissa loved to see Mr. Velarde was because he sometimes brought his son, Julian, who was in Melissa's class at school. When Julian came to the bar, the two children often played hide and seek and enjoyed empanadas. If they could find a spare quarter lying on the bar floor, they'd dance to a song on the jukebox.

"Not today, I'm afraid." Mr. Velarde looked at Melissa apologetically but didn't offer an explanation.

Melissa shrugged and headed back to the kitchen when she heard the distinctive sound of the bar door opening again. There were often two rushes on Fridays: the before-dinner rush and the after-dinner rush. For a reservation with fewer than a thousand people between the Apaches and the Hispanic residents, twenty to thirty regulars crowding the tiny bar for most of the night was quite a lot. The quiet afternoon Melissa had spent watching rainbows glint off glassware would soon shift into an evening of loud voices, explosive laughter, and ear-splitting music. The smells of her grandfather's aftershave and the turpentine and sawdust solution he used to sweep the bar would be replaced by the astringent scents of spilled alcohol, body sweat, and cigarette smoke. It made the girl's stomach curl, but it never kept her from her work.

She peeked into her grandfather's office. It wasn't much of an office; it was more like a glorified closet, with a small desk, filing cabinet, and table lamp. She knew he kept records for outstanding bar tabs, food costs, and alcohol shipments in a locked desk drawer. Tucked along the wall was a sturdy cot where she found her brother, sound asleep.

Mischievous and energetic, Melissa's brother Mark was three years younger than she was. It was no wonder he slept the first part of the afternoon after his classes. That way, his orneriness meter would be full again and he'd be able to wreak havoc later in the day. His actions often caused her *abuela* to make the sign of the cross and pray. Melissa knew her brother's behavior had been extra bad when her grandmother would pull her rosary beads from her pocket and rub the shine off each bead.

Melissa plopped down next to her brother on the cot, rifled through her school backpack, and took out *La Telaraña de Charlotte*. She'd only gotten through a chapter or two of the book, but so far, she really liked the idea of a pig and spider who became friends. Why shouldn't people who are different from each other find a way to be friends?

Absorbed in her book, Melissa initially didn't hear the ruckus coming from the bar area. As soon as she did, she snapped the book shut and shot up, her brother still sleeping. She made a lot of noise, hoping Mark would awaken, but he only emitted a snore that was far too loud for a seven-year-old to make and flopped to his other side, his skinny limbs tangled all willy-nilly.

Melissa tiptoed into the hallway and found a spot where she could peek into the bar without being seen. A woman she knew as Ginny was causing a stir with her grandmother, who was holding Ginny's screaming toddler in her arms, just out of reach of his mother.

"I'm fine, Mrs. Mercure!" Ginny poked an index finger toward Melissa's grandmother and swayed on her feet. "Jus' need a drink is all." She stretched to steady herself on the bar but missed. She stumbled forward and kicked a barstool, sending it skittering across the floor. The sudden noise caused Ginny's son to holler even louder. Melissa couldn't stand to see Ginny act like that, but she couldn't look away.

"Seems you've already had enough to drink," said Gregorita, Melissa's grandmother, clutching the squealing toddler closer to her chest and patting his back. "Let me make you some coffee, get you some soup."

Without warning, Ginny threw an off-balance, weak punch at Gregorita. Melissa's grandfather reached across the bar, catching Ginny's fist in his hand.

"You know better than this, Ginny." His voice was calm, his eyes hard.

"Please." Tears streamed down Ginny's cheeks. "One drink. That's it. Then I'll be on my way. No harm done."

"I can't serve you when you're like this," Melissa's grandfather said, his voice soft and low. "You need to go home, get some rest."

"I'll take you, Ginny." Mr. Velarde reached out a hand that Ginny slowly took.

Gregorita peered down the hallway, somehow knowing Melissa was listening from the shadows. When Melissa emerged, Gregorita gently transferred the little boy to her granddaughter's arms.

"I'm going to put together a platter," Gregorita said as she hurried back toward the kitchen. Neither Ginny nor Mr. Velarde moved, knowing that Gregorita's proclamation meant for them to stay where they were.

The bar had its fair share of regular customers, many of whom had a relationship with alcohol that Melissa was just beginning to understand. It was their dependence on the drink that made people like Ginny cry when they didn't get enough or beg her grandfather to "put it on my tab" when they didn't have the money to pay that day. Sometimes the alcohol even caused them to become so forgetful that they couldn't care for themselves or their children.

Melissa looked into the wide, brown eyes of the child she held. He was no longer crying or wriggling. But his tears had streaked through a layer of grime on his face, his shirt was covered with holes and stains, and his diaper was well overdue for a change. No wonder the poor thing had wailed while his mother had focused on her dependency rather than on him. Melissa stroked his fine black hair and smoothed back the pieces that had stuck to his wet cheek.

Before long her grandmother appeared with a stack of foil-covered plates, which she loaded into the waiting arms of Mr. Velarde.

"Soup, quesadillas, enchiladas. Make sure she drinks a glass of water before you leave." She turned to Ginny. "I'll keep Ben overnight until you're ready to take care of him properly. You come get him in the morning."

"Clothes, diapers …"

Melissa's grandmother tenderly patted Ginny's sagging shoulder. "Don't you worry about a thing. You just go home. Eat, rest, and take care of yourself."

Once Mr. Velarde had escorted Ginny from the bar, Melissa's grandmother took Ben into her arms. "Now we get to take care of you, little man. First, let's get that face cleaned and that diaper changed. Then we'll see how you like *Abuela's* beans and rice. Not too spicy, I promise." She tickled Ben's tiny chin, making him giggle. Then she winked at her granddaughter as she took their guest for the evening into the kitchen.

"Can I help?" Melissa sidled up next to her grandfather. He'd just finished cleaning Mr. Velarde's empty glass and was wiping down the bar. Smiling, he tossed her the towel he'd been using.

Melissa wadded up the damp cloth and cleaned the bar top with large circles.

"Do you think you clean the bar a thousand times a day, or less?" Melissa asked.

Her grandfather laughed. "As many times as it needs it. Some days it's less than that, but other days it's lots more."

"That must be why you have so many muscles."

11

"I guess it is."

"*Abuela* doesn't have big muscles."

"Well, not in her arms maybe, but she does have a bigger muscle than any of us have. We just can't see it on her body."

"Which muscle is that?"

"Her heart."

Melissa wrinkled her nose. "Her heart?"

"Yes, she does so many kind things for so many people."

Melissa scrubbed, deep in thought. "She takes care of people's children when they can't, gives them food, and helps them if they need clothes or a place to stay."

"That's right. That's just who she is. She never thinks about it. She just steps in to help. It is hard for her to give up on someone who needs help."

"And that's why her heart muscle is so big, because it's full of love for so many people."

Her grandfather beamed. "Exactly."

At that moment her grandmother and Ben emerged from the kitchen. His hair had been combed, his face had been washed, and he wore an old Batman T-shirt Mark had outgrown. *Abuela* had also made sure to change his diaper.

"Thank you, *Abuela*." Melissa hung the bar towel over the rack behind the bar where her grandfather draped them.

"What for?" Her grandmother led Ben behind the bar toward the office area where Mark was sleeping. She held a coloring book and a box of crayons.

"For being a helper. For caring about so many people and me and Mark."

"Oh, my little one, that is so kind of you to say." Her *abuela* wrapped her arm around Melissa's shoulders. "When God gives as much as he's given to us, we must find a way to help others who need it. Jesus tells us to be charitable in the Bible, but when we reach out to others because we want to help them, it means even more to him because that means we've learned the virtue of charity and the importance of it. Charity becomes a part of us when we practice it."

As Melissa watched her grandmother enter the office with little Ben in tow, she realized she was right. Not once did her grandmother complain about the charity she so willingly doled out. Rather, it filled her with energy, kindness, and love. Melissa knew this was not only her grandmother's special gift but that it was hers as well. Plenty of people around her needed help. She promised herself—and Jesus—that she'd find a way to serve others. Soon she would find a reason even better than a grandmother's love.

Chapter 2

"Go left here." Melissa's grandmother pointed in the direction she wanted her husband to turn. He clicked on his signal and gently applied the brake, the old sedan slowing down.

It was mid-summer. School on the reservation and in the village was out, and Melissa, Mark, and their grandparents were on one of their special summer adventures. They were going to witness a miracle.

Their grandfather navigated the dusty desert highway as Melissa watched clouds of sand kick up from the back tires and half-listened to the gospel music on the Christian station her grandmother had found on the radio.

Except for the occasional tractor trailer, the two-lane New Mexico highway was mostly barren. Melissa grew sleepy as she gazed at the grand mountain ranges that surrounded them. It was as if God had taken a putty knife and sliced off sheaths of clay to reveal the markings under the stone. Each ridge was perfect, with a unique blend of red and orange hues and sharp rock formations. Smatterings of foliage stood starkly against the blue sky.

Before long, Melissa felt her *abuela* shaking her awake. No longer was she surrounded by statuesque mountains. She was now in a neighborhood of clapboard homes with green lawns and abundant trees. The reservation had plenty of trees, but those seemed spindly and starved compared to how lush these looked.

Their trunks were so wide, Melissa couldn't even wrap her arms completely around them. She noticed a mischievous look in her brother's eyes and knew he was itching to climb one and hide in the dense leaves.

"Now children, be reverent. We are here to witness one of God's miracles. We are so blessed that he finds a way to show his love for us in these very special ways." Her grandmother took one of Mark's hands firmly in her own. She placed the other hand on Melissa's shoulder. Her husband led the way up the concrete path to the front door and confidently knocked.

A short, stout woman with curly auburn hair and pearl eyeglass chain opened the door.

"Good afternoon. My name is Alejandro Mercure. This is my wife, Gregorita, and our grandchildren, Melissa and Mark. We understand that Christ blessed you with a miracle, and we hoped you'd be kind enough to allow us to witness it also."

This wasn't the first miracle that Melissa and Mark had witnessed, and Melissa was certain it wouldn't be the last. Several times each summer, her grandparents would gather the children in the car in search of miracles. They never failed to visit the church in the town where the miracle had occurred, either. She had no idea how her grandparents uncovered these miracles, but they always found some. And today's, Melissa was sure, would be similar to the others she'd seen.

"Welcome. Please come in. I'm Consuelo Morales." The woman stepped aside, allowing Melissa and her family to enter the home. "I'm very happy you're here."

The inside reminded Melissa of a gingerbread house. It smelled of cookies and lemon wood polish. Knick-knacks carefully placed on lace doilies adorned every piece of neatly arranged oak furniture. A white Persian cat was curled on a floral-patterned damask settee, lazily swishing its long tail. Melissa instantly felt comfortable.

"Jesus showed his face to us in the kitchen," Consuelo commented as she led the way through the family room to the compact kitchen at the rear of the house. She picked up a plate of cookies from the counter. "I've just baked these. Snickerdoodle." She bent over to offer the plate to Melissa and Mark.

Both children looked at their grandmother for permission. When she nodded, Melissa and Mark reached out.

"One each, please," Gregorita instructed the children.

"Thank you," Melissa and Mark said in unison, their mouths full of cinnamon cookies as Consuelo started to explain the miracle.

"After repainting the kitchen, I noticed that over by the stove the paint just hadn't dried the same as everywhere else. So I kept looking, trying to figure it out. My brother was outside cutting wood to update the trim, and he came running in. He said to me, 'Consuelo, that's no bad patch of paint. That's the face of Jesus!' So I followed him outside, and I stood where he'd been standing, looked through the window into the kitchen, and lo and behold . . ."

Consuelo stopped talking so she could bless herself with the sign of the cross. "It was Jesus. You can see him right here through my kitchen window!"

Melissa's grandmother gasped and blessed herself with the sign of the cross, too. Her grandfather looked at the spot of paint in question by the stove. Melissa followed him. To her, the area looked like an uneven section of plaster that when covered with bright yellow paint appeared simply to be dull shadows, not the precious face of Jesus Christ.

Consuelo held open the screen door that led from the kitchen to the backyard. Melissa and her family walked down three small steps onto an emerald green, spongey lawn. Consuelo led the family to a giant oak tree whose trunk was twice the diameter as the one in the front yard.

"Now, if you just look through the kitchen window there—the one that has the sink right below it—then tilt your head to the right just a little bit, you'll see his face." Melissa and her family stood under the oak tree, their heads tilted sideways and eyes squinted against the sun as they looked for the face of Jesus on the freshly painted wall.

"*Dios mío!*" Melissa's grandmother exclaimed as she pulled her rosary beads from the purse that was hooked in her elbow. She clutched them to her chest and began rubbing one of the beads and praying in whispered Spanish.

Out of the corner of her eye, Melissa caught Mark opening his mouth. Knowing he was going to say something rude, Melissa kicked him lightly in the shin. He scowled, but at least he didn't say something that would get him in trouble.

After her grandmother had prayed, her grandfather approached their hostess and reached for the wallet in his back pocket. "Can we give you a donation? For your time?"

Consuelo brushed him off with a wave. "That's kind of you, but no. I feel strongly that this is a blessing that I was given to share with everyone else. It's Jesus's way of showing us that he truly is everywhere. And when he sends his spirit to one of us, we must share his message with everyone. He lives in each of us. We just need to show that to each other in our own unique ways."

Many see proof of God's presence in the wonder of a star-filled sky or in the majesty of a brilliant sunset. Melissa learned from her grandparents to feel God's love in what many would discard. They saw the love of Jesus in a bad patch of paint. Melissa wasn't sure the breaks in the paint were Jesus, but she could tell the image gave Consuelo and her grandparents a reason to smile and hope.

"I plan to help as many people as I can," Melissa said. "Everyone who needs it."

It was something she'd been thinking about for a while. Her grandmother was a constant source of help and encouragement for their community. Her grandfather was the captain of their local fire department and served on the water company board to ensure that the people of the village and the reservation received clean, healthy water. And her Uncle Alex worked with educational and social needs on behalf of the Native American and Spanish populations in New Mexico. In fact, the last time he visited Melissa's grandparents for dinner, he had talked about creating a Health and Education Livelihood Program (HELP) to serve those in need. Melissa knew her grandparents were excited about this prospect, as they offered daily prayers for Uncle Alex's success. So the willingness to sacrifice and collaborate in order to help others was well represented in Melissa's family. She just needed to discover her own path to do that.

Consuelo patted Melissa tenderly on the shoulder. "I'm glad you've already figured out Jesus's role for you. It may not always be easy, but if you're confident in where he is leading you, you'll never go wrong." Melissa could never have guessed the path the Lord would reveal.

Chapter 3
North Long Beach, California | 1969

Melissa loved the swoops and swirls of the letters she created and the strong, sweet scent of the ink. She liked watching it bleed into the fibers of the paper, like how the red and orange dawn sun bled into the dusky morning sky. Each day after she completed her schoolwork but before her mother came home from her job at the Southern California Gas Company in Compton, Melissa lined up the bottles of ink and laid the pens and various tipped nibs in another neat row. She took a stack of her special unlined paper and practiced calligraphy. Writing poems was soothing and helped keep her mind off the struggles in their Long Beach neighborhood.

Melissa and her mom lived in a small row home that was just big enough to fit Mark and her grandparents when they drove from New Mexico to California to visit. Melissa had moved to California to live with her mother almost a year earlier, leaving Mark, her grandparents, and the small village of Lumberton behind.

Melissa's mother, Juanita Theodora Teddi

Melissa's mother, Teddi, had started working at the gas company as a typist. But with southern California's large Hispanic population, Teddi had quickly recognized the need for Spanish-speaking service representatives and brought it to the attention of the higher-ups, who'd agreed and promoted her to customer service representative. The good news for Teddi and Melissa was that this promotion came with a salary increase and much-needed medical benefits. The bad news was that Teddi often worked long hours and Melissa came home to an empty house after school. With Mark still too young to take care of himself, Teddi had felt it made the most sense to leave him in New Mexico and bring Melissa to California with her.

Splitting a family in such a way was not customary in Hispanic homes. Most Hispanic families lived together or in very close proximity, and if one person moved or left for an opportunity outside the community, the whole family packed up and followed. It was just their way, and it wasn't questioned.

That was how it had been in Melissa's family until recently. Although her family had lived in New Mexico since the 1600s,

Melissa and her brother were the first generation to speak English as a first language. When her Uncle Alex decided to leave New Mexico and get a college education in Los Angeles, Melissa's grandparents and mother had gone with him and set up a home for all of them there. When the rest of the family returned to New Mexico, Teddi had chosen to stay in Los Angeles and keep Melissa with her. This enabled Teddi to have a career she would not have had in New Mexico. But things were not so good in the neighborhood where they lived.

As Melissa continued to practice her calligraphy, the usual cacophony of street noise was suddenly punctured by a loud pop followed by three or four other pops in quick succession. An engine revved. Tires screeched. Melissa's pen fell to the floor, red ink pooling onto the carpet.

Melissa jerked her head toward the picture window at the front of the house. Fear ran up her spine. She saw neighbors racing down the street as a couple of men shouted angry, foul words at each other. A woman screamed. Another started wailing, sobbing and asking Jesus why this had happened. And then another pop rang out.

With little thought, Melissa threw herself to the ground, rolled under the coffee table, and covered her head, curling into a tight ball. She'd heard the pops before and knew what they meant. Unlike in Lumberton, New Mexico, pops here weren't fireworks. They were gunshots.

She heard more screams and cries of anguish. Melissa wanted to know which of her neighbors had been hurt—and why. Had people been targeted? What had they done that was so wrong that someone felt the need to drive past their home and shoot them? She wished she could help, but she was so fearful she couldn't move. She remained hidden under the coffee table, shaking uncontrollably, until she heard sirens.

Swirling blue and red lights patterned on the living room wall as Melissa slowly moved from her hiding place. Curious, she peeked through the curtains. It seemed that whoever had been hurt had already been loaded into the ambulance. The lady from a couple of houses down was talking to a police officer, waving her hands to make a point.

A few hours later, Teddi burst through the door. Melissa was snuggled in a quilt on the living room couch, reading a book to distract herself.

"I heard about the shooting. Melissa, my darling, are you OK?"

Melissa shrugged, trying to act nonchalant. "It was pretty scary," she finally said. She didn't want to tell her mother that her heart was still fluttering, that she'd thrown up two or three times that afternoon, or that her stomach had been twisting and churning since the shooting.

Teddi stroked Melissa's cherubic cheek and brushed a strand of thick black hair from her daughter's face. "I'm so sorry I wasn't here."

"I did what you told me to. I hid under the table."

"Good." Teddi sat on the couch next to her. "That's very important. These bad people may not be aiming for you, but they could miss where they're shooting and . . ."

"I know, Mom." Melissa rolled her eyes. "This isn't the first time this has happened. And I doubt it'll be the last."

Teddi sighed. "I know."

Melissa's fear morphed into anger, and her eyes shone with unshed tears.

"Drive-by shootings, houses getting broken into, muggings, cars being stolen. Is this really normal, Mom? Are we supposed to live every day just trying to stay alive?"

Teddi grabbed Melissa and held her tight. Melissa wanted to pull away, but she realized her mother was just as scared as she was. She knew her mother wanted to protect her and felt guilty she hadn't been there. Both of them also knew that if the shooter's aim had been off, Melissa could have been the one fighting for her life in a hospital.

"This is our community, my love."

Melissa pushed her mother away. "Well, our community needs some help. Because this just isn't right." She stormed out of the living room, threw herself on her bed, and sobbed. She refused to come out of her room for hours, even with the promise of dessert after dinner.

Melissa didn't sleep well that evening. Almost daily she'd overhear her neighbors speak of drug deals, thefts, and murders. Long into the night she worried about the constant violence in her community.

Chapter 4
North Long Beach, California | 1973

Melissa boarded the bus for Phineas Banning High School in Wilmington. There was a public high school that was closer—one that was clean and had high-quality teachers and state-of-the-art teaching tools—but it was saved for the white and Asian kids. The black, Samoan, and Latino kids were sent on a bus to Phineas Banning.

An earthquake had ravaged Phineas Banning, and the county had rendered it condemned and considered it uninhabitable. So students attended classes in tiny bungalows that had been erected on campus. Nearly 3,000 kids shuffled among the small classrooms while walking past a building that was partly in rubble and ruins. It was a constant reminder that the repairs to their school had been neglected.

Melissa stepped off the bus, her head down and her bookbag slung tightly over her shoulder. She'd learned not to look at some of the other students, especially the kids who were in gangs. She never knew when they'd take exception to the way she looked at them. Melissa had heard of a student who'd been attacked in the boys' bathroom. Rumor had it he'd been beaten so severely that the surgeons couldn't repair all of the broken bones in his face, so he'd always have a disfigurement. Melissa didn't know how true that was, but she did know that the student hadn't been to school in months. And that's how she'd learned to stay out of the bathrooms. Always. No matter how badly she had to go.

"Hey, Melissa," someone from behind her yelled. Melissa adjusted her bookbag, lowered her head further, and hurried toward a group of students she hardly knew so she could blend into the crowd. She didn't want any trouble. Not today. Not here.

She hoped to camouflage herself in a crowd of two tall guys wearing denim jeans with dobby striped shirts and three girls with neatly plaited hair, their brightly colored wide-legged pants and striped fitted tees reflecting early 1970s fashion. But before she could do so, she felt a tap on her shoulder. Melissa turned slowly to see who was there.

"Hey, sunshine. Why didn't you stop? I was calling you." Malcolm Dwyer shook his head as he looked at her.

"I'm sorry," Melissa said. "I'm just in my own world, I guess."

"Well, quit thinking about the Partridge family and be aware of what's around you. You catch my drift?"

Malcolm subtly nodded toward the troublemakers who tended to congregate in the large grassy area between the bungalows. In the past some of them had called her names that were so foul she didn't dare repeat them. Others had asked her to relinquish her virtue to them. Each time she saw those guys, she'd purposely take a different path to class, even if it was longer.

Malcolm was one of the few friends she'd met at Phineas Banning. Melissa knew he was looking out for her and that he might be part of the reason the gangs mostly left her alone.

"Chill," Malcolm said. "It's all good. Let's get to Mrs. Monahan's class before we're late."

Melissa picked up speed, her short legs no match for Malcolm's longer ones.

Other classes were riddled with continual disruptions from unruly, bored students, but Helen Monahan had a special way of keeping the attention of the students in her social studies classes. A Mexican woman who wore a bun high on her head of tousled curls, Mrs. Monahan could make anyone behave with only a withering glare. That look reminded Hispanic students of their mothers and grandmothers who didn't hesitate to use their own versions of that glare to keep their families in line. Her kindness and gentle spirit let every student know she truly cared. Not all teachers at Phineas Banning were as revered as Mrs. Monahan.

The bell signaled the end of class. Melissa stood and began to walk toward the door.

"Melissa, may I speak with you a moment?"

Melissa stopped and turned immediately at her teacher's voice. "Have I done something wrong, Mrs. Monahan?"

"Quite the contrary. I saw something, and I wanted to discuss it with you. I think it's something you'd like."

"Check ya later," Malcolm said quietly as he passed Melissa on his way out the door.

"Thank you for thinking of me, Mrs. Monahan."

She pulled a sheet of paper from a corner of her desk and handed it to Melissa.

"A scholarship?"

"Yes. Occidental College. It's a small liberal arts school, but it's quite acclaimed for its academics. It's nearby in Los Angeles, so you wouldn't be far from home but could continue your studies."

"But I was planning to be a secretary, and that doesn't require college. I mean . . ."

"A secretary is a terrific career. I know your mother started out that way, right?"

Melissa nodded. "But with a degree from a four-year college, and one with so many options, you could do other things."

Melissa studied the paper her teacher had given her. The photographs took her breath away. She loved the sleek white walls of the Herrick Interfaith Center and the gorgeous sculpture in front that looked like a dragonfly floating in a fountain. She was awestruck by the decidedly Mediterranean feel of the campus, with its covered walkways and tile roofs. Melissa could almost already imagine herself there, participating in philosophical debates and poetry slams. It seemed like a place where scholars from all backgrounds learned together.

"I know it's intimidating. And it's scary to think you can be something more than what you thought you were capable of." Mrs. Monahan put her arms around Melissa's shoulder. "But I believe in you. I believe you can do anything and be anyone you want to be. If you wanted to go to the moon, I believe you'd make it there."

Melissa glanced again at the paper. "I want to change the world."

Mrs. Monahan smiled at her. "Then you will."

When Melissa got home from school that afternoon, she immediately retrieved the information about the Occidental College scholarship program from her backpack. She read it a dozen times and then started the application process. Then, not for the first time, she had second thoughts. "Where will this take me? Can I do this? I can go, but can I graduate? Then what? What place is there for a Hispanic girl with a college degree? Am I crazy?"

Chapter 5
North Long Beach, California | 1980

"Did you go to church today, little one?" Melissa tucked the phone between her ear and her shoulder as she pulled on a pair of canvas sneakers. Long, black strands of hair kept falling in her face, and she pushed them behind her ear impatiently. She was hardly a "little one" anymore. Melissa was an adult now who'd not only received a full scholarship to Occidental College but had also graduated.

"Yes, *Abuela*. I did go this morning."

"And what did you think of the Gospel reading?"

Melissa bit her lip. She had to admit she hadn't been paying much attention that day—or on any Sunday lately, really. She went to church because she didn't want to disappoint her grandmother, who inevitably called every Sunday around noon. She'd been checking out women's shoes, dresses, and hairstyles, not the statues of the saints, the sermon, or the quality of the instrumentalists, which were always topics her grandmother asked about.

"As always, it was thought provoking, but I would really love to read the passage from the Bible myself and the passages around it to form my own idea of what it means."

They had a Bible in the house, but neither she nor her brother had been permitted to look at it. As her grandmother would remind

31

them, the Bible was holy and they were not. So the Bible sat on the shelf, a very pretty and ornate book with a careful log of the family history of marriages, births, and deaths but with its spine hardly cracked.

"When are you leaving to visit your uncle?"

Melissa cradled the phone against her ear, deftly maneuvering the spiral cord to a more favorable position as she added a few small toiletries to her suitcase and snapped it shut.

"My plane leaves later tonight. Around eight." With the time change and the long flight from California to Washington, D.C., Melissa would arrive in the wee hours of the morning and was prepared to spend the entire day with Uncle Alex, whose evolving political career had taken him to Washington.

"You listen to your uncle, little one. He has been in Washington long enough to know the area well. Don't go off on your own. Stay close."

"Yes, *Abuela*." Melissa was used to these conversations with her grandmother. She knew that her friends who didn't understand her culture would find such discussions tedious or even unnecessary. But in a Latino household, family was everything.

"How's Mark?" Melissa was anxious to change the course of the conversation away from church. Unfortunately, Mark was another difficult subject.

"The same." Melissa's grandmother sighed. "He was so angry when he came back to New Mexico after living with you in Los Angeles. And that anger hasn't gone away. He still feels the effects of being out there. Being different. Being less than."

"That didn't mean he had to turn to drugs." Melissa knew how angry her brother had been. She couldn't count how many times he'd told her he'd been pulled over and detained by police officers because he was more brown-skinned than many of the others around him.

"I know, my dear. And I thought that bringing him back here to New Mexico might help him, but he just got right back into the situation he was in when he left."

"I pray that the Lord finds him."

"So do I. I'll never give up praying for him."

"Melissa, we need to get going," her mother said, peeking her head into Melissa's room.

"Thank you, Mama." She couldn't wait to discover Washington, D.C., and to see what had drawn her uncle there.

Chapter 6
Washington, D.C. | 1980

T he Carter administration. Melissa couldn't believe it. She stared at her handsome uncle, dressed in his pressed navy suit, and thought he looked just as presidential as the president himself.

"I'm the undersecretary of agriculture for President Carter," her uncle explained as he straightened his New Mexican bolo tie.

Always jovial, he winked at her, and pride grew in Melissa's chest. Diversity was finally settling into Washington, D.C. Opportunities for people of color, particularly Hispanics, were increasing with far more speed than in decades past. And now, here was her very own uncle, serving on President Carter's cabinet.

"So what do you do? What does that mean?" Melissa asked.

"Well, it's a little hard to describe, but the department I work for has to make sure we have enough food and resources to sustain the population. We have to measure population growth and use science, public policy, and any other resources we can manage to help support our farmers and keep our agricultural system competitive. We do sell some of our crops to other countries, and we need to make sure we have a balance between what we sell and what we eat."

Melissa could do little but stare at him in awe.

"We have a new program in place where we train former farm workers as paralegals. Much of this was brought about because of Cesar Chavez. Do you know much about him?"

"His family was from Mexico, right?"

"He's American, from Arizona, but yes, his parents were Mexican immigrants."

"Didn't he fight for better conditions for farmers?"

"Yes, he helped to develop the United Farm Workers union and is working to reorganize it and make it more visible by reaching out to the public. This program that's being developed as a collaboration with the Institute for Law and Justice is a result of his work."

"It sounds fascinating."

Alex picked up his briefcase. "It might be worth you looking into. If you're interested in social justice and lawmaking, maybe this would be a place for you to get a start."

***

Melissa sat on a bench on the National Mall, picking at apple slices as she considered her future. Witnessing the fast-paced lifestyle of Washington, D.C., and the efforts of those who worked hard to make real change had been exhilarating. If she went to law school and became one of the lawyers who graced the grounds of the U.S. Capitol, she could fight for those whose voices weren't heard. She could fight for the people who'd lived alongside her in the row homes in Long Beach. She could fight for the people who lived on the Apache reservation. She could fight for single parents like her mother, who'd struggled to make ends meet, and for those who turned to drug abuse like her brother. Melissa felt confident she could make a difference if she rooted herself in government.

She listened to the women's fashionable heels clopping on the cement as they made their way back to their government positions after lunch. Their hair was pulled back in taut, practical buns, and they wore fitted suit jackets in professional blues, grays, and tweeds with matching knee-length pencil skirts. She admired not only the sharpness of the way they dressed, but also the look of determination on their faces. Melissa could tell these women had purpose. They belonged in Washington, and so did she.

***

As Melissa poured herself a cup of the predictably awful sludge that passed for coffee, she felt a gentle bump to her hip. This was the typical greeting of her friend Mary Matthews, a paralegal at the Institute for Law and Justice.

"You're starting law school when?" Mary asked as Melissa dumped far too much sugar into her cup and stirred it with a skinny, red plastic straw. She took a sip and frowned. If she added any more sugar, her coffee would be crunchy.

"I'll go to law school once they can learn to brew a decent pot of coffee around here."

"I always keep a jar of Folgers crystals at my desk for emergencies like this."

The two ladies sat in scuffed orange melamine chairs at a chipped white laminate table. All of the other seating areas in the breakroom were just as shabby.

"I'm waiting to hear back," Melissa said.

"A school back in LA?"

Melissa nodded. "It's the only school I applied to."

Mary ran a finger along the rim of her cup. "Why didn't you apply somewhere out here? You have so many contacts. So many people who could help you."

"It's hard to understand." Melissa thought of her mother, whom she hadn't seen in what seemed like forever. She thought of her brother, who was struggling with the drug abuse that had plagued him since he was a teen. She wanted to make meaningful change, but she also had a responsibility to her family. Especially now that her *abuela* had passed and her grandfather was living with her mother.

Mary slapped the table, making it wobble. Melissa's coffee sloshed over the side of her cup. "Try me. I understand things way better than you might think."

Melissa sighed. One of the best things about being involved with a program focused on Hispanic farm workers was that most of the people she worked with were also Hispanic. They shared not only her passion for elevating the Latino community but also the cultural values that were often difficult for people of other cultures to understand.

"I have to get back to my mother. You know how it is. When a Latina makes a life choice, it becomes the family's choice too."

Mary shrugged. "Times are changing. Women have the opportunity to pursue new careers other than the traditional female choices like teachers, nurses, and secretaries. You shouldn't feel badly about wanting to reach for the stars and the moon. You deserve it!"

Melissa shook her head. "You don't understand. Our family lived in this tiny little community in New Mexico for twelve generations. It wasn't until my grandparents' generation that our family actually spoke English!"

Mary laughed. "For real?"

"Yes! It was an insular community. We ran our own government—in compliance with state laws, of course—once New Mexico became a state. We ran our own businesses, all in Spanish. My Uncle Alex was the first in our family to ever leave New Mexico and go to college. Most people in my family had never left the state."

"What did they do for a living?"

Melissa fingered the sleeve of her wool sweater. "Sheep farming, mostly. But my grandparents wound up inheriting a bar in a little village next to an Apache reservation, and my mother and uncle lived with them there until Uncle Alex went to college in Los Angeles."

"And let me guess—like a good Hispanic family, they all went to LA together."

"Exactly. However, my mother met my father, and when the rest of the family went back to New Mexico, she stayed behind. She and my father had me and my brother, but eventually they got divorced."

"And your mother didn't move back home?"

"No. She was determined to make a life for herself in LA. And she did. My brother and I spent a lot of time in New Mexico, though, while my mom was working and making a home for us. I moved back in with her when I was about twelve or so."

"Wow. Your mom was so brave."

"So were my grandparents." Melissa took a sip of her coffee. "There's an old family story. While I was being born, my grandparents got in the car and headed off for California. My Uncle Alex stayed back to take care of things while they were gone. After I was born, Uncle Alex called and told my grandparents that during their trip, their house caught on fire. They lost everything. And my grandparents said nothing at all to my mother until the following year."

"Why?"

Melissa shrugged. "That was just their way. They were all about family. The house didn't matter to them. That Uncle Alex was safe, that my mother was fine, that I was healthy . . . that's all that mattered. To them, a house is just a dwelling. Family lives far beyond brick and mortar walls."

"And what about you?"

Melissa stared into her coffee cup.

"My family is everything to me. But there's a part of me that needs to reach beyond the importance of my family and do something that's going to be impactful to someone else. I want to be the catalyst that changes someone else's life for the better. And I can't do that if I remain at home, afraid to take chances and disappoint my mother."

"And how do you think she feels about that? About taking chances?"

Melissa laughed. "I didn't think I would be speaking with a therapist during my break today."

Mary shrugged, then reached across the table and squeezed her friend's hand. "I am many things, my friend. My talents with psychotherapy have barely been tapped."

Both women laughed. Then Melissa sighed. Her friend had posed a good question. Melissa couldn't be a lawyer who fought for social justice unless she were permanently housed here. Her dreams had flourished during her time in D.C., and they couldn't possibly look the same elsewhere. How would her mother feel if Melissa created a career for herself in Washington, D.C.? Was it even possible for a Hispanic girl who'd grown up in a remote area among Spanish and Apache people to become a lawyer and make a difference in how impoverished people lived? But first, there was law school.

Chapter 7
Los Angeles, California | 1985

Melissa stared at her name on the diploma, written in beautiful calligraphy right under the name of the school she'd graduated from: Loyola Marymount University School of Law. Pride welled within her. She could hardly believe she'd successfully completed a law degree. She silently thanked those who had influenced her, especially the Hispanic lawyers she'd met while serving in Washington, D.C., who had not-so-subtly swayed her to apply to law school.

"Time for dinner, Melissa," her mother called from the kitchen.

Melissa placed the framed diploma lovingly on her bed and joined her family.

Her mother had prepared a large meal of Melissa's favorites in celebration of her achievement. The table was set with their best dishes. A fragrant pot of meat and potatoes and a plate overflowing with homemade empanadas waited on folded dishtowels on the counter for Melissa, her brother, her grandfather, and her mother. All of them sharing a family meal happened far too rarely. The fact that her mother had spent so much time preparing this feast brought tears to Melissa's eyes.

Melissa threw her arms around her mother and squeezed tight.

"What is this, *hija*?" Teddi laughed. "You haven't been this way since I got you that doll you wanted so badly when you were nine years old."

"I'm just so grateful, Mama." Melissa wiped at her wet cheeks. "I never thought I would graduate from college. And then I never thought I'd graduate from law school. This is a dream come true."

Melissa melted into her mother's arms as Teddi hugged her once again. When she opened her eyes, she saw her brother take an empanada from the pile and pop it into his mouth. He chewed with a sharp set to his eyes, his jaw working hard.

"Mark?" Melissa pulled from Teddi and turned to face her brother. "Are you OK?"

He swallowed hard, his Adam's apple bobbing up and down. "Fine."

"Well, let's all sit down while I dish out the food." Teddi turned toward the counter, stuffed her hand into a mangled orange oven mitt, and lifted the pot of meat and potatoes. She scooped an oversized helping and spooned it onto Melissa's plate. She followed with servings for Mark, her grandfather, and herself.

Melissa and Mark sat in silence. Melissa stared at him expectantly, hoping he'd tell her what was bothering him. He slouched in the yellow padded seat, arms crossed, artfully avoiding her gaze.

"I'm sorry, Mark," Melissa spat out. Finally, he turned his gaze toward her. She could see it was full of hurt and anger.

"What have you done to me, Melissa? Why are you sorry? Are you sorry for being perfect? The perfect daughter. The perfect student. The perfect lawyer. Are you sorry for that?"

"I should have been here for you, Mark. I should have maybe— I don't know—stayed closer. Not traveled so much. Not spent so much time away."

"I didn't need to be babysat." Mark stuffed another empanada in his mouth and chewed furiously.

"Look," Teddi interjected. "Now is not the time."

"But it is, Mama." Melissa placed a hand over hers. Her mother sighed and Melissa watched as her shoulders slumped. She turned once again to her brother.

"I need you to know that I love you. And that I'm sorry that I was on my own path."

"And my path was the wrong one, right? Because you weren't there, that's why I got involved with drugs? With the wrong crowd? If you'd been there, that would have all been different then. Is that what you're saying?"

Melissa shook her head. "Maybe, I—"

"Well, it wouldn't have been." Mark shoveled potatoes into his mouth. "I would be the same screwup whether you were there to see it or not."

"I don't believe you're a screwup. I think you have a lot of good in you. You made some mistakes, sure. We all make mistakes."

"Except for you."

Melissa's eyes filled with tears. "That isn't fair, Mark. I worked hard. I earned everything I got. I wasn't handed a single thing."

Mark shook his head and stood from his place at the table. He wiped his mouth with his napkin and threw it across his still-heaping plate of food.

"I gotta go." He leaned in and kissed Teddi on the cheek. "Thank you for dinner, Mama. Not sure when I'll be home." He didn't look at Melissa as he headed for the door. She jumped when the door slammed.

"Melissa, I am so sorry. Your brother is just . . ."

"It's OK, Mama. You don't have to justify his actions. He's his own man. He always has been, always will be. I do feel guilty that

I haven't been there for most of his life. I love him, I really do, but I just don't know him very well."

"I understand that, *hija*. There's a lot of space between you in years. When you're young, three years is a huge gap. You were in high school here in California while he was in New Mexico with your grandparents, still too young and unpredictable to take care of himself. And it wasn't your job to look after him. I did my best for the both of you."

"I know you did, Mama. And I tried too. But I went against our culture. I went to college, to law school. I should have been here."

"And you think I followed our tradition?" Teddi stirred some potatoes around on her plate. "When Alex came to California to go to school, you know your grandparents and I joined him. But after I met your father, after Alex graduated, I refused to go back to New Mexico. That was very much against our culture. But I wanted to stay here with your father. I needed to get some space from the family and stretch my wings somewhere other than New Mexico."

"What did *Abuelo* and *Abuela* do?"

Teddi looked at her father, who was still scooping food into his mouth. "Your *abuelo* helped to build us a home. It was his way of making sure I was safe even though he wasn't there to protect me himself."

"So he supported you leaving?"

Teddi shrugged. "In a way, I guess. Our culture often encouraged the men in our families to achieve, while the women were more successful in their household duties and childrearing. But your *abuela's* side of the family, the García side . . . well, they were a little bit different. They still wanted their families to stay tightly knit, but they did make sure that the women in the family had skills in voice and fine arts."

"So is that why your parents were OK with you leaving? With you getting a job?"

"I suppose that's the case." Teddi studied her daughter closely. "I know that they were certainly supportive of it with you. They supported your education and your work with Uncle Alex. We are not only Hispanic, but we are American too. It is a marriage of both cultures that enabled them to help you with your education and support me staying in California and working outside of the home while I raised my children."

"There's a way to do both."

Teddi patted her daughter's hand. "Yes, there is. We can find a way to keep our Hispanic culture alive and thriving while we find a path, a calling, for ourselves and strive toward the American way."

Her mother's words resonated with Melissa. "That's awfully exciting."

"Yes, it is," Teddi affirmed. "And you, with your work ethic and your education, are poised to do it even better than I did. Be more successful than me. You, my daughter, will be something special. You will follow a path that is your own and will accomplish a great many things that impact this world. I have no doubt of that."

Melissa's mother leaned across the table and pulled her daughter into another hug. At that moment, Melissa knew her mother was right. This world was bright and open, welcoming Melissa. All she had to do was embrace it.

Chapter 8
Sacramento, California | 1985

"Rubber chicken dinner. Who wants in?" Miguel, a National Urban Fellows grant intern, called out. A handful of interns, including Melissa, looked up from their desks. Others kept their eyes glued to their paperwork and typewriters.

The Sacramento office of Senator Ralph Estevez[1] buzzed like an expertly tended hive. Each employee had a role, and constituents were well served. New to the office, Melissa was eager to learn the lay of the land. Although she'd initially been slated to work with a different senator in Ohio, Senator Estevez had felt that Melissa's skill set and Hispanic background would be better utilized in his district in Sacramento. Melissa couldn't have been more pleased. She was able to stay in California, where her mother was, and she'd have opportunities to connect with her fellow Hispanics who served the surrounding Latino communities.

"Come on. Someone has to do this. It can't be me again." Miguel waved his arms, attempting to solicit some interest.

"I'm still suffering the consequences of the rubber chicken I had a month ago," muttered Shirley, another intern. She rubbed her

---

[1] The senator's name has been changed, as he was not consulted for this biography.

47

belly for effect, but it didn't seem to dissuade Miguel, who was now walking up and down the aisles of desks.

He stopped at Melissa's desk with a smug look on his face. "Hi, newcomer."

"I may be new, but I'm well trained. And one of the first things I learned was to be cautious about you."

"But I'm just here to ask you on a date."

"Am I supposed to be flattered?"

"I would be. I'm asking you to go to a gala with me."

"A gala? It's 1985, not 1785."

Miguel smirked. "Fine. It's a dinner for some company that wants the senator to support them, so they invited him to this quasi-charity event hoping to woo him with rubber chicken, stale mashed potatoes, and baked Alaska."

"Well, when you put it that way," Melissa shrugged, "how can I refuse? What company?"

"Since you asked, it's a waste removal company that's trying to secure a contract. I guess they figured if they partnered with a charity and invited some of the important people in the community, they might get a leg up on winning the bid."

"So they decide to spend all this money on a big to-do in an effort to woo important people hoping that, when it comes down to making a decision, Senator Estevez and the other people will remember the charity event where they were served a flaming dessert and will sign on the dotted line?"

Miguel laughed. "Yep. Pretty much exactly like that."

"And Senator Estevez doesn't want to be a part of this himself?"

"He's got way too much on his plate," Shirley interjected. "If he went to all of the events he was invited to, he'd never get any actual legislation done. So we get to go in his place." She grimaced and rubbed her belly again. Melissa finally agreed but hoped there was a vegetarian option on the menu.

"I'm picking you up at six. No last-minute stomach bugs or headaches or anything like that. Got it?" Miguel pointed a finger at Melissa as he walked backward toward his desk.

"I can't wait." Melissa's stomach did a flip-flop. She'd only been part of this fellowship program for a couple of weeks and was just getting the hang of the position and its responsibilities. Despite that, she was looking forward to representing the senator's office that evening.

***

Melissa smoothed the skirt of her best red dress and draped the starchy white napkin across her lap. Miguel had picked her up at her small apartment, which was located only half a block from the Sacramento capitol building and had escorted her to the banquet room like a perfect gentleman. Melissa had learned in their short car ride that, while he often came off as goofy, his heart was in the same place as hers. They were both in this to make real change in the Hispanic community.

The room was decorated just as Melissa had expected, with white tablecloths covering about twenty round tables. Matching napkins sat like teepees on top of salad plates; vases of red, white, and yellow carnations with sprigs of baby's breath adorned each table. A podium stood in the center of the room atop a small riser covered with the same dull, patterned carpeting that ran wall to wall throughout the rest of the room. Heavy gold-colored drapery covered the windows, and chandeliers dangled from the ceiling.

An overly efficient, tuxedoed waiter cleared Melissa's salad plate almost before she'd taken her last bite. She glanced at Miguel, who wiggled his eyebrows at her in an "I told you so" gesture. Melissa fought back a giggle.

Just as the speaker started discussing the service routes the waste management company would take, a steaming plate was laid in front of her, with broccoli spears and gravy-smothered chicken and mushrooms over rice.

Miguel leaned in. "Huh, no twice-baked potato. I'm gonna miss that."

Once again, Melissa had to fight her instinct to laugh. She took a bite and quickly realized why Miguel had referred to the meat as "rubber chicken."

"And once the routes are complete, the waste will be deposited in a newly constructed landfill here." The presenter used her pointer to indicate on a map a large red dot smack in the middle of a poor Hispanic neighborhood. That area already housed an old trash dumping site that was now leaking methane gas. From Melissa's perspective, adding another landfill would only create an even more toxic neighborhood.

"That's a terrible idea," Melissa said, leaning in to talk to Miguel. "I was with them until this. This neighborhood is in Senator Estevez's district. It needs to be cleaned up before anything else like this gets put in there."

Miguel shook his head. "We can certainly take this back to the senator and let him know our thoughts."

"I was under the impression that we were here to help his constituents, right?"

Miguel shrugged. "Some of them, I guess."

"What's that supposed to mean?"

Miguel placed a hand on Melissa's arm. "Not to offend you, newbie, but you have a lot to learn. It's not all about the right thing to do. There are promises made, favors extended, and backroom sweetheart deals made."

"I can't believe that Senator Estevez would pay attention to any of that. He's all about trying to help the poor areas of his district. That's what he ran on and why he won."

"Yes, that's true. And I believe Senator Estevez has good intentions. I really do. But there are other things at play—things behind the scenes that we don't see, and neither does the public. Things aren't always done for the most altruistic of reasons."

Melissa didn't get much sleep that night as she thought of the community that would be impacted if the deal went through. She remembered how in California her mother had to wash their white sheer curtains a couple times a month to remove the black soot that wafted into their home from the nearby oil refinery; once again, a "dirty" project was being snuck into a poor area. She tossed and turned thinking of the air quality, the health effects the community could suffer, and the dangers of potential explosions. She couldn't allow this to happen. She vowed to speak with the senator the next morning.

***

"Good morning, sir. I'm here for our meeting."

Melissa knocked on the door frame of Senator Estevez's office, a file of notes and a stack of newspapers tucked under her arm. Part of her job was to read *La Opinión*, a daily, influential Spanish-language newspaper, and report back to the senator about the issues his constituents were facing so he could address them.

"Ah, Melissa. Please come in and have a seat."

She sat on the edge of the creaky, uncomfortable leather-bound chair.

"I heard you went to the waste management affair last night." Senator Estevez clasped his hands in front of him, regarding Melissa through the thick lenses of his black-rimmed glasses. Melissa noticed his kind, brown eyes and thick head of hair that was beginning to show a few silver strands. He wasn't a large man, but he could effortlessly take command of a room, a crowd, or any one person. His persona was perfectly suited to a position of influence, especially politics.

"It was lovely," Melissa said. "Except for one thing. The company is proposing a landfill be placed in a community near Dodger Stadium that is already having air quality issues because of an abandoned dumping ground that's producing unhealthy levels of methane."

Senator Estevez rubbed his chin with a forefinger and thumb. "This is a disturbing concern."

He sighed, and Melissa took the pause as an opportunity to disclose her thoughts. "I did some research. Long-term exposure to methane gas can lead to respiratory problems, including pneumonia, heart issues, memory loss, headaches, and sometimes even epilepsy. Some of these health issues can be permanent. And there's nothing preventing people in this community from breathing it or having it enter their homes. Until it's fixed, they have no choice. It's not right to add something else to their neighborhood that can further affect their health. And besides that, it's a flammable gas. Depending on the concentration in the air, it could easily ignite, and then what?"

The senator nodded. "I see your point, Melissa. And I can see how this program could compromise the best interest of the people who live in this neighborhood. But there's some good that will come out of this too. We need the community to keep in mind how much this new plan will also cut their taxes. So the conservation efforts that this company brings to the table can be a benefit."

"Sure, once the methane is cleaned up in the neighborhood. Do they have any plans to do that before they implement these other strategies?"

"I know they do. We're still working up the legislation and still negotiating the terms, so I can make sure the cleanup that's needed is part of that. This is some terrific work that you've done to bring this to my attention."

"Thank you, sir." Her stomach flipped and flopped. She was grateful for the praise, but she knew there would be more to the story. Miguel had given her fair warning, hadn't he?

"Now, one thing we are going to need to do is get some public support for this, and I'd really like for some of that support to come from the neighborhood where the waste site is proposed."

"No one there is going to approve of this!" Melissa's cheeks began to flush. She could feel the heat rising up the back of her neck.

"Of course they will. Like I said, there are a lot of benefits to their community. And even more that we still need to discuss. I know you can get some sound bites and video clips of people who would be quite enthusiastic about this. No one can possibly feel badly about reducing waste, cutting costs, and lowering taxes. We could even try to make sure that some of the savings from this program is brought back into the community itself."

Melissa bit her lip in an attempt to suppress the lingering anger she felt on behalf of this struggling Latino community and shrugged once she'd composed herself. "I suppose we could earmark this money for some positive change in this community. Apply the extra money toward education? Green space?"

"Terrific idea! I love the thought of bringing green space to that area since it's such a concrete jungle. And it really connects with our plans around conservation." Senator Estevez reached a hand across his desk. Warily, Melissa took it, and they shook. Proposed legislation wasn't necessarily granted in its original draft state, but she had to trust the senator was a man of his word and would fight for the cleanup and the benefit of this community.

"So, how about by the end of next week, we have those video and audio clips from community members who are in favor of this new waste management plan. Can we do that, Melissa?"

"Yes, Senator."

"And I will add everything we talked about to the legislation I'm writing up, and we can move forward and get this bill on the books and get everything rolling. Sound like a plan?" He stood from his chair.

Melissa stood, too. "Thank you, Senator."

"For what?" "For listening to me. For hearing my concerns for this community. I know that your district is large and your constituency is comprised of many different types of people from high and low socioeconomic levels and different cultures." Melissa pressed a fist against her mouth, willing the tears brimming in her eyes to go away. This was not the place to get overly emotional.

She cleared her throat. "So, anyway, I wanted to say thank you for keeping even the poor and forgotten communities, those that could be taken advantage of, in your sights."

"Well, Melissa, they are all under my watch," Senator Estevez reassured her. "I want to make sure that they all get what they need."

Melissa felt a glimmer of hope as she left the senator's office. It hadn't been a bad meeting, but she knew more work needed to be done. The senator needed to convince a lot of people to clean up the area before the new waste management company affected the community. A gnawing doubt pulled at her. Was he up to it?

Chapter 9

"I'm all for the landfill in this community because I feel good about this waste management company's commitment to the environment. Their service is going to lower our taxes and keep our community clean."

The middle-aged Latino man spoke into the microphone Melissa held just out of range of the video shot. He was dressed in his work overalls, which sported badges with his name and "Mick's Mechanical." Melissa and Greg, the camera operator employed by the senator's office, had set off to the community that would be affected the most by the new waste management company.

"Thank you so much, Juan," Melissa said gratefully. "I think the senator is going to love this clip."

"You tell him that we are looking forward to his promises to clean this place up. We are counting on him." Juan gave her a thumbs up.

"I'll be sure to let him know, my friend."

She handed him a poster board that said, "I support Waste Management Services!"

"Don't forget, I need a group of you to stand over here on this corner and hold up your signs in support of this new program, OK?"

Juan congregated with eight or nine other people who had agreed to appear on camera holding signs in support of the cause.

Afterward, Melissa and Greg moved on to a local *mercado*.

"We want to hear how you feel about the new waste management firm that's coming in here," Melissa explained to the owner. "Before they come in, the senator is planning to get the methane gas situation fixed, and your community will be cleaner because the system this firm has will create less waste, and it's cheaper, so you'll save money in taxes. The senator says that the money that's saved will be put back into the communities, so he's hoping that maybe there'd be a park here."

The owner of the convenience store happily agreed to comment on camera.

"Our community needs a pick-me-up," he said. "We've been stagnant for so long with no one willing to help us. It's like we've been forgotten in favor of the rich. But we count, too, and with this plan, it shows that Senator Estevez cares about us. He's listening to our voices too."

Before the day was over, Melissa had clips of at least a dozen people speaking positively about the new waste management company. Greg had carefully shot footage to make it look like an even larger gathering had been holding up signage in favor of the senator and his plan. The videos would look terrific in news clips, and Melissa knew that was exactly what the senator wanted. She just hoped he would uphold his promise to focus on the well-being of the community.

✳✳✳

The rubber chicken bounced around Melissa's stomach along with the chocolate torte she'd had for dessert. She tightened her grip on Senator Estevez's arm as she walked him out of the Elks Tower ballroom.

The fundraiser for a local hospital had been better than most of the events Melissa had attended since her internship began. But the benefits of the grant—the free housing, the adequate stipend, and the résumé boost—sometimes didn't seem worth the efforts she had to take to keep the senator's name out of the papers for inappropriate conduct. That night, for instance, she'd watched him flirt with waitstaff and polished women in glitzy dresses.

"Melissa, why are you so good to me?" The senator's words were slurred, his eyes mere slits as they entered the elevator. The last thing she needed was for any reporters to catch wind of his inebriated condition or for his political opponents to snap photos for their ads. She also hoped the hospital's billing coordinator, a beautiful, young Hispanic woman named Flora, would brush off the senator's incessant flirting and not report him for harassment. Rumors had swirled around the breakroom for weeks that this behavior was taking a toll on the senator's marriage.

"Everything's fine, Senator. Just stand tall, and let's walk to the car quickly. It's parked out front, and we will get you straight home."

"One of the ladies mentioned an after-party . . ."

"I have to insist, Senator, that you return to your home. Your family's waiting."

"Did anyone ever tell you that you're a stiff, Melissa?"

The elevator dinged and the doors opened. Ignoring the senator's insulting comments and incoherent grumbling, Melissa managed to drag him through the lobby to the car.

"Let's get him home, please," Melissa told the driver.

"Take me to the party, Rick," the senator slurred. "There's a couple hundred bucks tip if you get me there."

Rick looked in the rearview mirror and raised his eyes at Melissa. She gave him a subtle shake of her head, and he put the car in drive.

The hum of the tires against the road and the gentle bumps as the vehicle passed over manholes quieted the drunken man, and he slumped against the door, his head knocking softly against the window. As the senator let out an obscenely loud snore, Melissa sighed and once again told herself that this wasn't what she'd signed up for.

Just a few days earlier, the senator had celebrated the passage of the waste management bill. Melissa had been excited, too, since this was a piece of legislation she'd been part of. She'd spoken to residents, organized media events, and proudly stood next to the senator as he'd explained the benefits this would bring to the area. She, too, had become convinced that the plan was a positive for the community. She'd felt good that this would not only clean up the neighborhood and bring tax breaks but would also eliminate the methane problem she'd been so concerned about. It seemed to be a win—until she read the bill. As soon as she did, she marched into the senator's office.

"Senator, I just read the waste management bill, and I'd like to speak to you about it."

"Of course, come on in. Have a seat."

Melissa sat on the edge of the uncomfortable chair and took a deep breath. "Sir, we'd discussed the benefits that this bill would bring to the community. We dug deep, got community support. We promised them the methane would get cleaned up and that there would be no adverse effects to the community. I helped write the talking points you delivered to those people, the ones that helped convince them that this bill was good." Melissa felt tears prick her eyes, but she held them back. She wanted to handle this professionally.

"Now I read the bill, and it seems everything we'd added to help those people was taken out. And now, instead of just a landfill, there will also be an incinerator?"

"Yes, to help reduce the amount of waste that would go into the landfill."

"But sir, this will further add to the issues they are having with their air quality. Now whatever carcinogens the incinerator produces will mix with the methane." Melissa shook her head. "I can't believe there was no compromise to be made on this bill."

"Look, I know this is hard to understand, but sometimes in order to make progress, we need to have some sacrifices. Give a little to get a little. You know what I mean? This community was the best place to put this incinerator."

"Why? Because all of the people there are poor? Because their lives aren't as important as the rich people making the decisions for them?"

A flash of anger crossed the senator's face. "I serve all of my constituents. Sometimes the decisions I have to make aren't popular. And they're never easy. The waste management company is helping out my campaign that way. Even though we haven't been able to help this community now, I can stay on track for making it up to them later. I resent you questioning my integrity."

He averted his eyes dismissively and picked up a folder from his desk. "Now, if you don't mind, I do have things to do. And if I'm not mistaken, so do you."

Melissa stood up and walked out of the senator's office with her back straight. Her steps were confident and powerful, even though inwardly she was quivering.

"What just happened?" Mary whispered, leaning across her desk toward Melissa.

"It's nothing, really." Melissa sucked in a deep breath and fumbled through the latest issue of the *LA Times*.

"Come on." Mary stood up.

"Where are we going?"

"We're grabbing drinks from the vending machine and sitting on the benches out front. And you're going to tell me what's bothering you."

"Oh, that?" Melissa jerked her head toward the senator's office. "That isn't worth talking about."

"It's not just that." Mary looked concerned. "Stuff's been going on with you for weeks now. You aren't as exuberant as you've been in the past. You haven't walked in each morning with your usual energy."

Melissa gave her friend a thin smile, a half-hearted attempt to prove her wrong.

"I don't buy it, lady. Come on."

Soon the two women were seated on a park bench, enjoying the California sunshine and sipping their sodas.

"I just didn't think working for the government would prove to be so, so . . ."

"Criminal?"

Melissa laughed. "If it's within the auspices of the law, it isn't criminal, is it?"

Mary shrugged. "I guess that depends, doesn't it?"

"On what?"

"Your morality. Look, I believe when the senator got here, he was totally altruistic in his intentions. I think he thought he could save the world. Then he learned that power and money make those altruistic ideals virtually impossible. Everyone around here has an agenda. Everyone has ulterior motives. Everyone can be bought off for the right price."

"And the poor people suffer?"

Mary shrugged. "Sure. Who else would it be? Not the rich people who decide where their money's spent. Not the middle class. They have the largest number of voters, and they have just enough money for people to notice them because they pay most of the taxes. So who's left?"

Melissa crushed her empty soda can. "Half of the poor people that are taken advantage of by this thinking are either uneducated and have no real idea what's going on or can't speak English. They don't have the skills to get good jobs to move from their poverty into the middle class, or they don't have the education to get them there. So they have no choice but to live in communities that become the dumping grounds for all the bad stuff. I thought by becoming a lawyer and taking part in this internship I'd learn ways to help people. But instead, I've learned more about the ways in which they can be taken advantage of or get hurt."

Mary touched Melissa's arm. "Look, I still believe I can do some good. And I know you can too. It's just that politics is a game that not everyone's cut out to play. Some of us . . . well . . . we need to rethink how we are best suited to help people. Maybe for you, it's not here."

"Is it for you?"

Mary shrugged. "Yes, it is. I know it is."

"Then I wish all the best for you. I can't begin to imagine how strong you are to know this world of vipers is the place for you."

"You'll find your place, too, Melissa. I know it. It may not be tomorrow, but it will happen."

Melissa had heard that before. And she'd also heard that Jesus would hear the words in her heart and guide her to the right place. Each time she went to church, she wondered how and when her calling would come and what God would ask of her. No matter: With the Lord, she would be up to it.

Chapter 10

Melissa nodded at the people in the crowd to acknowledge their polite clapping. She'd just addressed a gathering for representatives of Spanish-speaking churches. Melissa's internship was almost over, so she was making the best of it, writing speeches for the senator, and speaking on his behalf when he was too busy to attend himself. It was more rewarding than working on proposals that wouldn't help people and certainly more fun than dragging the tipsy senator out the back entrance after events where he'd had a few too many cocktails.

Melissa had come to realize during her internship that the level to which she'd hoped to help people couldn't be achieved through local politics or the judicial system. She knew government wasn't the right place for her.

Melissa stepped from behind the podium, pushing together the index cards she'd used during her speech. The next speaker would be up shortly, so she quickly made her way off the small riser and wove her way through the tables to her seat.

The other presenters that afternoon spoke about the resources their communities needed yet lacked. Hearing church representatives tell so many stories of need made Melissa's heart hurt. But it also helped her recognize that the place where she could make real, meaningful change was within the communities themselves—communities like the impoverished mountain village and the violent neighborhoods of North Long Beach where she'd grown up. It was on those streets and among those people where she could make a real difference.

After the speeches had been delivered and the desserts devoured, Melissa gathered her belongings to make her way back to the senator's office. She had much to tell him, including several ideas for grassroots efforts in the communities where his constituents lived. As she slung her handbag over her shoulder, she noticed a man coming toward her.

"Good afternoon." The man stuck out a weathered hand. Melissa took it, marveling at the sheer strength that went into his shake.

"I enjoyed your speech today. You work with the senator?"

"I'm an intern." Melissa cleared her throat. "And thank you, very much."

"I could tell that you have a passion for helping people, especially those who are suffering in underserved communities."

"I do, yes." Melissa beamed. She was thrilled that her true meaning had gotten through the political babble she'd had to layer into her speech.

"My name is Pastor Esaul. I am the pastor of a Spanish-speaking Lutheran church here in the Los Angeles area. I would like to invite you to our church sometime if you don't already have a church. But even if you do, we are quite welcoming to guests." He reached into the breast pocket of his tailored suit jacket and pulled out a business card.

"Thank you." Melissa placed the card carefully into her handbag. "I would love to visit your church sometime. I must admit, I haven't found one yet that makes me feel like I'm at home. And I believe that's how a church should feel, right? If you're going to visit your Father at his house, you'd expect that it would be a place that brought you comfort."

"I can't disagree with that," the pastor said.

"Well, I look forward to visiting your church soon," Melissa declared.

"I'll be waiting for you." He extended his hand once again for Melissa to shake and turned and walked toward the exit.

Melissa took the card the pastor had given her, looked at it, then put it back in a small, zippered compartment in her purse. Numerous times throughout the week she'd do the same thing. She couldn't push El Redentor Spanish Lutheran Church from her mind. It felt as if she'd been to every Catholic church in California, but none of them had been a good fit. She did attend one regularly, but it was because it had the shortest masses, not because she had any real affinity for it. Something new, especially a Spanish-speaking church, might suit her.

That Sunday, Melissa walked up to the church slowly, looking again at the card to make sure she had the address correct. She was used to urban churches in highly populated Spanish-speaking areas being jammed into the nooks and crannies of any real estate available to them. This church was no exception; it was as if a ranch home from the 1960s had been duct-taped to an active corner *mercadito*. The organ music coming from the church contrasted with the Mexican *norteño* tunes from the store next to it. People strolled up and down the bustling street, and Spanish chatter surrounded her. The scene reminded Melissa of her roots—of the small northern New Mexican village where she'd grown up and of her ancestors, who spoke nothing but Spanish in their little alcove of northern New Mexico for many generations.

Melissa carefully pulled the door open and slipped into the shadows in the back. Music permeated the room. The worshippers were singing a hymn she knew—in Spanish. A flood of emotion washed through Melissa. This was what she'd been searching for.

With tears in her eyes, Melissa sat in the back pew. She felt the notches and scratches in the weathered oak wood from the countless people who'd sat there before her. Hearing the words of

Jesus sung in her native language made her heart swell. She found herself singing along, her voice growing louder with each refrain.

Sunlight filtered through the orange stained-glass windows and cast a soothing glow throughout the church. The pastor stood from his seat and walked to the pulpit as the hymn ended. In a deep, thundering voice, he read the words of Jesus Christ. Melissa was rapt.

"In Hebrews, God says, 'Keep on loving one another as brothers and sisters. Do not forget to show hospitality to strangers, for by so doing some people have shown hospitality to angels without knowing it.'"

Pastor Esaul raised his hands to the congregation of about a hundred people. "Each of us is responsible for helping our brothers and sisters. How do we do that? We can do that in acts both big and small. If someone is sick, bring them a meal. If someone is in need of a coat, lend them yours. If someone needs a ride somewhere, offer them a ride in your car. If someone is grieving, offer a sympathetic ear. If someone is lost, help them find their way. Jesus leads the way for us. He died but rose again from the dead. His life guarantees all who believe in Him and are baptized will rise from their grave. Jesus will help you and me find our way in this life too."

Esaul walked partway down the aisle that separated the two rows of pews. As he spoke, he would often pause to touch the shoulder of one congregant or the arm of another. Melissa was impressed by the way he engaged everyone. She loved how he encouraged his congregation to give to one another as a way to strengthen their community, not just in church, but on the streets as well.

Before she knew it, the swelling organ music ceased after a dramatic crescendo, and the congregation began to leave. Melissa loved the sounds of the rustling crowd as people gathered their belongings—the chatter, the laughter, the squealing of small children.

"Don't forget to take an empanada from the table before you leave," Pastor Esaul called over the crowd. "The Hernandez family was kind enough to make them for us today."

Melissa stayed in her pew and watched as several congregants approached the pastor. He greeted everyone with a brief embrace or handshake as if they were long-lost friends he hadn't seen in years. As the crowd around him diminished, he caught sight of Melissa.

"Well, you made it!" His booming voice echoed through the church.

"It seems I chose a good day to come. That was an impactful sermon about loving others as you love yourself, as God loves us all."

"Sometimes our congregation needs some reinforcement in that area. This is a very poor community, and they don't have much to give. At least not much in the monetary sense. But they still need to understand the ways in which they can be charitable." He waved a goodbye to someone behind Melissa.

"I feel like Galatians 6, verse 2 says it all: 'Carry each other's burdens, and in this way you will fulfill the law of Christ.' If we share in one another's times of need, then when our time of need comes, we will never have to worry. All of our burdens will be lessened through the help of others."

"Galatians. I'm sure I heard that verse before, but I didn't know that's where it came from." Melissa's face reddened. She hadn't meant to blurt that out, but it was true.

Pastor Esaul's eyes widened. "I'm surprised you aren't familiar with Galatians. It's a marvelous book."

"I'm sure it is. I've actually not read the Bible."

He motioned for her to sit down. "Talk to me about it. Why is that?"

Melissa settled into the pew. "Well, my grandmother kept a family Bible, but it was never for reading. In fact, when I asked her to read it, she'd look at me as if I had suddenly turned from a child into some sort of evil fairy tale creature. She'd tell me that the Bible wasn't for reading because only priests could interpret Jesus's words. She said that they went to seminary and that meant that they are closer to God than we are, so we are to listen to them when they read us the words of Jesus. But that never really settled well with me."

"Why is that?"

"I feel that while we often need the help of someone ordained to get into the real spiritual depths of much of the Bible, I think that every person can find comfort from it and can learn lessons through their own devotion. I think that messages gained through one's reading of the Bible can be personal messages that they need at a certain time in their life. That's something that a priest can't necessarily give someone, in my opinion."

"Have you felt this way for a while?" he asked.

"All my life," Melissa admitted. "It wasn't until I got out on my own that I realized how unfulfilled I was spiritually. I'd spent a lot of time thinking that I was meant to be a lawyer, a figure in the social justice movement for marginalized communities, but I was so disheartened by the politics that went along with it that I knew I was on the wrong path. My trajectory had to change. In time I came to realize part of that change needed to come from finding a new church and finding myself spiritually again."

Melissa indeed had found herself a new church. She started attending El Redentor regularly, and as the months passed, she realized how much she loved spending time with the congregants. All were Spanish-speaking immigrants who were hesitant and insecure when immersed in the English-speaking community around them. But once they were in their church and around others who spoke their language, they could be themselves. Melissa had heard many stories of highly educated people in the congregation who'd been quite successful in their countries. But when they came to America, they couldn't speak the language fluently and didn't qualify for the well-paying jobs they'd been educated to do. One congregant she knew was a chemist who was now working on an assembly line to make money to support his family. She could see the weight these people bore and their fear of failing their families.

***

One afternoon, Melissa sat in her favorite chair with a cup of chamomile tea and her Bible. Each time she got the chance, she'd study the Bible, finding passages that spoke to her and her place in the world.

She'd learned so much about Scripture from attending El Redentor. In this church, Melissa felt like part of the community, deeply connecting with the other worshippers, and most importantly, with Jesus himself. She'd found ways to use her leadership skills, too: She headed up the women's circles, kept watch over the Sunday school program, and helped minister to those in need.

The telephone rang, snapping Melissa from her thoughts.

"Hello?" she asked.

"Good afternoon. Is Melissa available?"

"Yes, yes. This is she."

"My name is Sandy Hente, and I serve with the Pacific Southwest District of the Lutheran Women's Missionary League. We are an auxiliary of the Lutheran Church—Missouri Synod, committed to supporting each woman as she uses her unique God-given gifts while ministering to people all around the world."

"Yes," Melissa croaked. "Excuse me. Yes, Ms. Hente, it's an honor to speak with you."

"From where I sit, it's an honor to speak with *you*. I've heard about all of the amazing work you're doing at El Redentor Spanish Lutheran Church in Panorama City. The church is flourishing, and you've reached out to so many within the community. I was hoping that you'd agree to be our mission speaker at the League's convention in San Diego."

Was this really happening? Had she really just been asked to speak about her tiny Spanish-speaking congregation to hundreds, maybe even thousands, of women? Immediately her mental wheels sprang to life. This was an opportunity to build support so that more ministries could be planted to serve the large Spanish-speaking community in Southern California. Melissa knew this was an important area of growth for the LCMS.

"I would be delighted!"

"Great! We will be thrilled to have you there. Let me give you the details."

Chapter 11
1992

The day before Melissa left for San Diego to speak at the Lutheran Women's Missionary League (LWML) Convention, four Los Angeles policemen were found not guilty in the beating of Rodney King. Riots and looting had broken out—violence Melissa would have to drive through. She knew the women at the convention would understand if she didn't want to risk driving through neighborhoods wrought with violent protests. But she'd been asked two years earlier to speak about her work with El Redentor, and Melissa felt obligated to honor that commitment. Sandy Hente had been so encouraging, even sending Melissa handwritten notes of encouragement, and despite the sacrifice to herself, Melissa didn't want to let Sandy down.

The ride was easy until she reached the outskirts of Los Angeles. Melissa thought about the reports she'd seen on television the night before and was hearing on the radio as she drove. The unrest, the rioting, the looting—the stories made her sick to her stomach. But she understood the outrage. She felt it too. It was just that something like this shouldn't seem possible in the United States.

Even though the windows were rolled up and the air conditioner was on, the corrosive smell of smoke seeped into the car. Clouds of black smoke billowed over buildings. Orange flames licked at the sky. People holding signs that read "Black Power," "Rodney

King," and "F**k the Police" screamed their messages from street corners. They edged their way toward Melissa's car, with fists in the air. Melissa's hands trembled, but she placed them firmly on the steering wheel. She kept her head forward, avoiding eye contact, not wanting to give anyone a reason to approach the car. Though she understood and sympathized with the pain of this community, she knew that people who were so deeply hurt could lash out even at those who supported them.

Shaken and near tears, Melissa pulled up to a concrete barrier in the middle of the street. It was laden with graffiti and vile words—the words of a community that had been cut deeply. Two military guardsmen stood at the barrier. Dressed in camouflage, with thick bulletproof vests, helmets with face shields, and rifles resting on their shoulders, the guards were an intimidating sight. Melissa didn't know whether they were there to help or hinder the situation.

"Ma'am, you can't get through here." One of the guards reached the car and knocked on the window with a knuckle.

With an unsteady hand, Melissa rolled down the window partway. "I'm trying to get to San Diego. Is there another route I can take? This is the fastest way I know."

"Highway's the only route now. But from what we've heard, it's pretty backed up."

To Melissa, the guard looked like a child. His round blue eyes were wide with a trace of fear. Tufts of dark hair wet from sweat were plastered to his forehead, and his chin had barely a trace of a five o'clock shadow. Melissa thought he was in his early twenties or maybe even still in his late teens. What did he know about the pain of the people of this community or the betrayal that African Americans across the country felt? How was this young man reconciling this tragedy within himself?

"Thank you," Melissa said quietly. "God bless you."

"Thank you, ma'am." The young man nodded his head. "Please be careful."

Melissa turned the car around and navigated through discarded protest signs, cardboard, broken glass from storefront windows, and scraps of burnt wood. Some of the residents gathered on the street corners cried; others yelled and pumped their fists. Doors were splintered and windows were cracked; some were boarded up with large sheets of plywood. All of them were covered with graffiti. Melissa passed the shell of a burned-out car that was still smoking on the opposite side of the road. She drove past as quickly as she could. Tan military transport vehicles were parked every few blocks. Army soldiers in riot gear stood in front of stores, looking imposing with rifles on their shoulders and pepper spray attached to their belts.

Melissa's eyes were full of tears as she prayed for the people of this community who were hurting, for everyone across the country who was angry, for the safety of the police officers who were trying to quell the riots, and for those whose brutality and prejudice led to this situation. She prayed she would reach San Diego safely. She also prayed for the future—that measures would be taken systemically so this wouldn't happen again. And of course, she prayed for Rodney King, a man whose health would be impacted the rest of his life because of the brutality he'd suffered.

As she drove further from the epicenter of the protests, the tang of smoke in the air began to lift. There was less graffiti, less military presence, and fewer people thrusting their fists in the air in anger. Melissa was soon able to take a deep breath and relax.

After what seemed like hours, Melissa found the on-ramp to the highway. The problem now was the bumper-to-bumper traffic. Melissa looked out her window at Los Angeles. Clouds of smoke billowed from the city, no doubt visible for miles. She said a prayer of thanksgiving that she was safe. For her, the dangers of the Los Angeles protests were past. But for so many others, the horrors were just beginning.

With only a few moments to spare, Melissa pulled into a parking space at the hotel and hurried toward the banquet room where the women of the LWML were gathered. She approached the reception table and received her badge, which listed her name, the church's name, and the title "Speaker." Chatter, laughter, and the sound of glasses tinkling permeated the room. Melissa marveled at the sight of so many women who shared a strong love for Jesus and a passion for missionary work. The room was a rainbow of A-line skirts with matching blazers, glittering brooches, coiffed and sprayed salon-done hair, and makeup-counter-at-the-mall perfect faces. In some ways the women reminded Melissa of the female lawyers she'd so admired when she lived in Washington, D.C. In other ways, they were altogether different. Melissa wasn't sure how she'd fit in here.

As Melissa smoothed down the skirt of the dusty pink suit she'd sewed for herself just for this occasion, she thought about the nightmares she'd recently had. She had dreamed of a white woman approaching her, pinching her cheeks, and saying, "Oh, look at this cute Mexican girl!" Then the woman, patronizing her, called her friends over, and they all pinched her cheeks, much like they would have done to a young child.

Melissa thought back to the kind notes of encouragement she'd received from Sandy Hente. She took a deep breath and promised herself she wouldn't let Sandy or El Redentor down. Sharing about the church's ministry was a great privilege, and these women had been so generous and gracious in inviting her to speak to their gathering.

As Melissa walked deeper into the room, music came over the loudspeaker. Melissa wasn't familiar with the hymn, but she thought it was beautiful. At once, all of the women in the banquet hall, about a thousand strong, burst into four-part harmony. Their voices blended seamlessly in an angelic chorus.

This must be what it will be like when I enter heaven, Melissa thought. Drawn by the faith of these women, Melissa was now at ease. While culturally Melissa and these women may have had some barriers, they shared too much in common spiritually not to accept her.

Once the hymn ended, the women continued their chatter. Melissa glanced at her watch. She was to speak in the next ten minutes.

"Excuse me?" Melissa approached two women who were nearby. "Can you please direct me to Sandy Hente? I'm the next speaker, and I'm not sure where to go."

"Oh, of course! Melissa!" One of the women pulled Melissa into a tight embrace. "We're honored to have you here to speak about your church."

"Honored to have me? My goodness, I'm honored that I was invited. I'm humbled by your interest in our tiny church." Melissa fought back the tears that pricked her eyes and absorbed the warmth of these two women. Never did she think she'd be so quickly welcomed into this austere group.

"I'll take you to Sandy," the second woman said, taking Melissa by the hand. "Over this way."

Melissa was led to a striking woman in a pantsuit that looked as if it had been tailored just for her. But what struck Melissa the most about Sandy was her youthful exuberance and the kindness that radiated through her gentle eyes.

"I'm pleased to meet you, Melissa. Finally!" Sandy beamed at Melissa, and her nervousness instantly disappeared. "So many of the ladies have been asking me about you and your mission. I'm certain you'll have a rapt audience today."

Sandy walked Melissa to the podium and tapped the microphone to ensure that it was live.

"May I have your attention?" The chatter in the banquet room quieted within seconds as the women settled into the fabric chairs that arced around the stage area.

"I would like to introduce our next speaker: Melissa Salomón from El Redentor Spanish Lutheran Church in the San Fernando Valley. There, Melissa ministers to the Spanish-speaking members of the community. She's here to talk to us about El Redentor's ministry."

Melissa reminded herself that this engagement was no different from the speeches she'd given on behalf of Senator Estevez. Speaking at a podium in front of hundreds of people was something she enjoyed. And as she began speaking about her church and her community, she felt her confidence grow.

"The funny thing about El Redentor Spanish Lutheran Church is that while everyone there speaks Spanish, no one is actually from Spain." Melissa was encouraged by the chuckles throughout the room. "We are a church community that ministers to congregants from eleven Spanish-speaking countries. Most of the people in our church are immigrants and find the English language a challenge. Coming to a church that ministers to them in their language not only makes them feel comfortable, but it gives them a place to go that provides them with the dignity they deserve but don't always find in their everyday life. At El Redentor, all churchgoers are part of a like-minded worshipping community. Here, they've found a welcoming place where they can know the love of God and share His love of with others in their unique culture."

Melissa talked about the organic ways the church provided outreach. She spoke of the women's circles, the Sunday school program, the prayer groups, and the congregants' work among their neighbors in their poor communities. She explained that even though church members didn't have much, they spared all they could for a friend or neighbor in need. Sometimes it was as simple as making a meal for an ill neighbor or giving someone extra clothing. No matter what one person or family needed, the entire El Redentor community was eager to help.

At the end of her speech, Melissa was overwhelmed by the applause she received. These women were more like her than she thought: daughters, sisters, mothers, and friends who felt a communal and personal love for Jesus Christ. At that moment she felt the connection: She fit with the LWML and the LCMS. She was assured of the love of Jesus. Was this the calling she so wanted from the Lord?

Chapter 12
Tijuana, Mexico | 1998

C louds of dust billowed behind Melissa's sedan as it
bounced through the potholed streets. She pulled into what
passed as a parking area in the commercial center that
included a tiny convenience store, a restaurant, and a couple of
run-down, abandoned storefronts. It was here, in Tijuana, that the
Lutheran Hour Ministries office in Mexico, called Cristo Para
Todas Las Naciones ("Christ for All Nations"), had just opened.
And she was to lead the office.

Melissa turned the key in the lock. Shirtless teens stared at her
from across the street, where they were drawing with sticks in the
dirt, their skin shiny from perspiration. Melissa pulled open the
door and slipped inside.

The office smelled of mildew and was as hot as a skillet.
Melissa feared she'd sizzle if she sat on the desk chair set up for
her. The place was far from elegant, but it matched this part of the
city: practical and dingy. The walls were in desperate need of fresh
paint. The ceiling puckered from water damage from a long-ago
storm. The cracked linoleum floor had probably been white at one
time but was now the same shade as a decaying tooth. A scratched,
gray file cabinet stood in one corner next to a water dispenser with
an extra jug.

In the back was a small room with a chair, table, and secondhand rug, likely intended as a breakroom or for counseling those who came to learn about the church and its programs. Melissa found a closet with typewriter paper, correction fluid, pens, pencils, and a paper tablet or two. A bathroom was across the hall with a rusty toilet and a drippy sink.

It wasn't quite how Melissa expected the office to look, but she knew that with time and some resources, it would become a haven for the community. Melissa took a tablet and pen from the closet and began to write down her thoughts on how to make this program work.

Melissa knew that although Tijuana's population was well over the three million mark, its residents were spread out. Impoverished people would often move to the outskirts of the city and build temporary homes from tarps, garage doors, scrap metal, or old planks of wood. Once they found work, made some money, and could afford better accommodations, they'd move further into the city. Public transportation was sporadic at best and was unavailable to most people, as were cars. Melissa realized many residents who could be helped by this office wouldn't be able to get there; it was too far. So the biggest issue would be reaching community members who didn't know what Cristo Para Todas Las Naciones was or who didn't have a way to get to the office to learn about Jesus.

The traditional model of LHM's international media ministry was to engage with interested parties, provide them with booklets on high-need issues, and refer them to nearby Lutheran churches. Unfortunately, there were few Lutheran churches in Tijuana, and those that did exist were not a viable option for many because of travel limitations. Melissa needed to think of ways to prove that outreach here was not only necessary but possible.

The first thing she did was seek out a local woman who was committed to the Lutheran church. Young Tere Montoya was in a Bible training program, and she was energetic and hard working—

a great fit for the ministry. Melissa and Tere decided to venture into the community, speak with people, and discover their needs. Their goal was to start small, to start local, and to then spread out. The two women walked Tijuana's dirt paths, sharing the love of Christ with the people they met. Along the way they passed transient housing, small shacks, and rundown homes in desperate need of repair. For every palm tree and colorful umbrella that lined the beaches at the nearby ocean, there were an equal number of families living in a tent, their worldly possessions fitting into a single garbage bag.

Partway into her walk one day, Melissa came upon an elderly woman seated on a rusty beach chair on her front porch. The stairs seemed rickety, and the house, once a beautiful blue, was now dull and faded. Shingles were missing from the roof, and a leaky section was covered with plastic.

"Hello!" Melissa waved.

The elderly woman squinted at Melissa. With gnarled, arthritic hands, she gripped the arms of her chair and lifted herself off the seat to look at Melissa more closely.

"We haven't met before," Melissa said.

The woman plopped back into her chair.

"I'm from the local office of Cristo Para Todas Las Naciones." Melissa pointed down the road to the cluster of buildings where her office was. "I was wondering if I could talk to you for a few minutes if you have the time."

The old woman waved Melissa closer. Melissa politely stayed at the bottom of the porch steps.

"Girl, I'm not going to be able to hear a word you're saying from all the way out there. Come up here."

Emboldened, Melissa carefully climbed the steps, which were much sturdier than they appeared.

"I don't know you, do I?"

Melissa took a seat on the wooden porch, her feet parked on the top step of the stairs.

"No, ma'am. I am the director of the outreach program that just opened up down the road there. Do you have a few minutes to talk to me?"

"What else do I have to do other than bake in the sun?" She lifted her arms in an "I don't know" gesture that made Melissa chuckle. She liked this woman already. Melissa discovered her name was Ana Maria and that she'd lived in this area of Tijuana all her life. She was now sixty-five years old and lived out her days watching the world pass by from her porch.

"Occasionally there are community meetings," Ana Maria explained. "The *diputado* from the *municipio* has some people come into the neighborhood to give us medicine or food. Sometimes they give us some other supplies, but that's only once in a while."

"How often do they come?"

Ana Maria snorted. "Not often enough. They tell me I have high blood pressure. They gave me medicine, but I've been out of it for two weeks now. I don't know if it helps or not, but if it does help, I want to get some more soon."

Melissa spoke with Ana Maria for about an hour, listening as she described her needs and the needs of the neighborhood, including medical care. Ana Maria gave her the mayor's address.

"I don't have the phone number because I don't have a phone, so why would I need it?" Ana Maria shrugged.

"That's OK. You have given me a wealth of information. And with what you've told me already, I plan to see the *diputado*. Let's see what God will do so that we can serve you and your neighbors."

"Well, young lady, I will look forward to that. *Gracias* for any help you can get us."

"I promise I'll do all I can to make this a better place for all of you." Melissa vowed she would make good on that promise and prayed silently for the help she knew she would need.

Chapter 13

Every day Melissa made the eight-mile trek across the border from her home in Chula Vista to the office in Tijuana. She was filled with worry—worry that the Mexican people would not accept her since she was not born in Mexico. She also felt she would be regarded with great apprehension, as skepticism of any non-Catholic church was common in Mexico. But that did not dissuade Melissa from her calling. Working in Tijuana gave her a new zest for her mission and filled her mind with possibilities, and she embraced the role wholeheartedly.

Melissa unpacked boxes of Spanish-language Bibles that she planned to distribute at the day's community meeting. After lengthy conversations with the *diputado* and his volunteers, Melissa had been invited to offer prayer and Scripture readings at the meeting. She'd moved, and her new church, Concordia Chula Vista, had graciously taken up an extra collection specifically for the outreach program in Tijuana; the church had purchased these Bibles. Melissa had also arranged for a large jar to be placed at the church for Mite Box offerings. She'd quickly become involved in the church's LWML group, whose members collected loose change (mites) for mission grants. The jar had filled up quickly, and the organization had voted to dedicate the offering to the outreach program. The additional funding had been a welcome boost to the struggling program, and Melissa was excited to see the mites at work.

Melissa stood to the side as volunteers dispensed medications in addition to dried beans, rice, flour, and other food staples. Before long, she saw Ana Maria in line. After receiving her medication, Ana Maria turned a little too quickly and found herself off balance. As she tried to right herself, she dropped the tote bag she'd been holding. Melissa moved in to help her.

"Oh, thank you so much," Ana Maria gushed as Melissa repacked the bag for her.

"Are these the pills you need? The ones you were telling me about the other day for your high blood pressure?" Melissa scanned the label on the bottle.

"I think so. It isn't the same name, but they told me this would work too."

"Use by December 1996." Melissa read from the pill bottle. "This is outdated by two years."

Ana Maria shrugged. "I stopped looking at expiration dates a long time ago. I'm sure these drugs have the potency to outlive me, and I'm not going anywhere anytime soon."

Melissa dropped the medication into Ana Maria's bag. "Well, I hope you'll stick around this afternoon. We are going to hold a Bible study after the medications are distributed if you're interested."

Ana Maria's face screwed up as she considered Melissa's offer.

"There'll be juice and cookies. I'm providing Bibles for everyone to use."

Ana Maria's eyebrows raised. "Well, I guess I have a little time to kill."

"That's great. I'm so happy you'll stay."

As Ana Maria moved to take a seat among the community members who were staying for Bible study, Melissa drew closer to the volunteers while they packed up the leftover medications.

"Excuse me. Can I ask you a few questions?"

One of the volunteers, a young man who couldn't have been more than twenty years old, looked up with a friendly glance. "What can I help you with?"

"A lovely woman I know from this neighborhood just got some medication. She says she has high blood pressure, but the medication you gave her was different from the one she'd been taking. And it was expired. Why did she get something different? And was her blood pressure even checked to make sure that's the medication she needs?"

The young man sighed. "Look, I'm just a volunteer. I do what I can to make sure that people get what they need, but often we don't have the same medications to give out month after month. And yes, sometimes they are outdated. We don't have the training to do any sort of health checks. We just go by what the patients tell us of their medical history."

"And you just trust that's accurate?"

He shrugged. "These people don't have the means or transportation to see a doctor, and many of them probably haven't seen one in years. We're equipped mostly to give out the basics: aspirin, cold medicine, bandages, that sort of stuff. But we give out prescription medication that's given to us by the government when we have it. It isn't always consistent."

"I'm not sure how this program is really benefiting the elders in this community."

Again, the young man shrugged as he zipped a large bag that contained the remaining medicine. "You're right. But it's better than nothing. At least that's what I tell myself."

Melissa and the young volunteer parted cordially, but the wheels in Melissa's head began to turn. How could she ensure better health care for the elderly in this neighborhood?

After the people who'd stayed had gotten their cookies and juice and had taken a Bible from the large stack she'd placed in the front of the room, Melissa asked them to turn to the Scripture she'd be reading from.

"Please find in God's Word 2 Corinthians, chapter 12, verses 9 and 10." She saw weathered hands turn to random pages and lined faces fill with confusion. Some placed their Bibles on their laps or on the empty seats next to them.

Melissa furrowed her brow. The Bibles were in Spanish, not English. She'd made sure of that before bringing them here today. But then it hit her. Many of these elderly people had not received a good education or even any education at all. Some likely didn't even know how to read. She took a deep breath.

"Many of you may be unfamiliar with reading God's Word, and that's OK. If you're more comfortable listening as I read, please do that." Melissa noticed many people relax their shoulders as she began to read the passage.

"But he said to me, 'My grace is sufficient for you, for my power is made perfect in weakness.' Therefore I will boast all the more gladly about my weaknesses, so that Christ's power may rest on me. That is why, for Christ's sake, I delight in weaknesses, in insults, in hardships, in persecutions, in difficulties. For when I am weak, then I am strong."

Melissa paused. She noticed some people were paying close attention, others appeared content, and others searched for more cookies. She knew that for many of these people, Bible study would be an important part of these community meetings going forward. She continued, sharing the encouraging and loving words of Christ.

As she boxed up the Bibles for use during the next community meeting, the *delegado,* Señor García , approached Melissa.

"You did an outstanding job with digging into God's Word today."

His high praise made Melissa blush.

"Gracias, Señor García . I hope that some of our elders found peace in the words of Christ."

"No doubt they did. I hope Bible study can become a regular part of this program."

"I intend to make it so. But I noticed a few things that concerned me—namely, the medication distribution and the unmet medical needs of the elders and others in this community. How can we make sure that the elders receive proper medical services? All we would need is a clinic-like format with blood pressure checks, wound care, basic techniques for self-care . . ."

Señor García stroked his beard in thought. "Presidente Fox has been working to massage government funding to ensure lower health care costs for those in need. But this clinic idea you've had . . . this makes a lot of sense until that can be instituted. What if there were a pharmacist present? Do you feel that would be helpful?"

"I know that culturally, many rely on home remedies or local pharmacists. So many have probably never seen a doctor. I know that many residents consider a pharmacist as good as a doctor, and the community members would likely take the advice given."

Señor García patted Melissa on the shoulder. "I'll work on finding a volunteer. And I'll see what we can do about getting non-expired medication for those in this community. With healthcare already a priority for Presidente Fox, I bet there is something he has put into place that we can access."

"Thank you, Señor." Melissa shook the *delegado*'s hand. She trusted he'd make good on his word. Nevertheless, Melissa planned to scour the surrounding areas herself for volunteers who could make this vision a reality. She knew if the pharmacist were a man, no woman in the community would allow him to examine her, not even to check her blood pressure, without qualified female volunteers present as well.

***

Melissa concluded the "friendship group," as the elder outreach program in Tijuana quickly came to be called, with a prayer. It had warmed her heart to see the room so full, and Melissa loved the peace that seemed to wash over the people as they heard the words of Christ. It was as if the tough years that some wore on their faces melted away when they connected with the Scripture readings Melissa shared with them.

"Thank you so much for being here today," Melissa said, smiling at each person who dropped a Bible into the box she held. "Don Francisco and Tere are both here today to offer anyone medical advice or services they need. And Don Francisco is also going to discuss another topic regarding the importance of self-care. Remember how last month he talked about the importance of adequate rest and techniques for getting a good night's sleep? Today he'll talk about pain management."

Melissa nodded to a couple of people in the crowd. "I know several of you mentioned to me that you suffer from chronic pain, so today Don Francisco will talk about things you can do at home to find relief."

Some people got up from their seats and stood in lines to talk with Don Francisco and Tere. Others stayed in their seats, awaiting the discussion on pain management. A few visited the spread of cookies and juice in the back of the room for the second or third time. Melissa finished collecting the Bibles and stood next to Tere. Even though Melissa couldn't offer medical advice and was not medically qualified to take blood pressures or listen to the women's hearts and lungs, she could answer basic first aid and nutrition questions.

As she got into her car after the meeting, Melissa rubbed her eyes and sipped the last of the cold coffee from her thermos, hoping it would give her a little extra energy.

The outreach program in Tijuana was moving along so beautifully that she was also working on adding a youth program. It was in its infancy, but she felt confident plenty of people would volunteer to get the program off the ground.

Chapter 14
1999

M elissa loved what she was doing, but her work didn't bring in enough money to buy or rent a home. She was grateful her mother and grandfather had welcomed her into their home. Her grandfather had moved in with her mother after her grandmother had passed away years ago and the property they'd held in New Mexico had been sold.

"It's time for dinner, *Abuelo*." Melissa grasped her grandfather's hand and placed another on his shoulder to stabilize him as he rose from his recliner.

Her grandfather gently patted her shoulder in a way that reminded Melissa of how he used to comfort her when she was a child living with her grandparents in New Mexico.

"You're meant to serve, Melissa, and to follow in the steps of Jesus himself. Your talents and abilities far exceed those of the average person, *mi'jita*, and you're using those gifts for the love of others. How many can claim their gifts from God are being used to their best potential?"

Melissa hooked an arm around her grandfather's shoulders and pressed him into a soft hug.

"You've always had a way of making me feel special, *Abuelo*. Your love and support and *Madre's* love and encouragement have always had the power to push me forward, even when I wanted to stand still."

"We love you, Melissa. And we see the good you're putting into the world. Your community would be much different without you making the impact that you are. Every act of kindness, compassion, or love affects others in a positive way." He pressed a kiss to the top of her head, and Melissa took his wrinkled hand in her own.

"Now, let's go eat. I'm starving." Melissa's grandfather tugged on her hand, nudging her toward the kitchen. Melissa helped her grandfather into his seat at the head of the table and took her spot next to him.

A wave of love washed over her. She thought of what her grandfather had said. Without her and the team, many elderly people in Tijuana wouldn't have heard the words of Christ or know how to read the Bible. They wouldn't be taking the right medications, understand the importance of self-care, or be getting proper rest. But despite all she'd already done, she knew she could make an even bigger impact. She just needed to find a new way to help.

Chapter 15
2001

"Heart to Heart Sisters. I love that!" said Marilyn McClure, her face bright as she scribbled in her notebook. Marilyn and her husband had been career missionaries in Guatemala, and she had a deep knowledge of the Lutheran Women's Missionary League because of the LWML's support of well-baby clinics in Guatemala.

"I hope this idea goes over well," Melissa said. The program that Melissa and Marilyn were proposing was innovative and vastly different from any other LWML outreach. Instead of focusing on community outreach like other programs did, Heart to Heart Sisters would concentrate on developing diversity *within* the church to serve the organization and widen its vision. The outcome, the women hoped, would be a diverse organization that could more effectively reach a diverse world.

Melissa's appointment to the national LWML Gospel Outreach Committee after a mere two years of involvement was unprecedented, as most women moved through the hierarchy slowly. She'd been invited to serve on the committee just a few weeks after she'd met the LWML president at the time, Virginia Von Seggern, at the organization's 1999 convention in San José. For years, Virginia had been in search of strong, faithful women of different cultures and backgrounds to lend a new, fresh voice to LWML leadership. During their conversation, Melissa had explained that her experience of serving in an ethnic ministry was isolating and that she felt connected to the greater church through her involvement with the LWML.

"How can we at the LWML change to welcome you, Melissa?" Virginia had asked. At that moment the dreams of the two women merged, and Melissa knew she'd found her place.

Melissa took a sip of her now-lukewarm coffee and placed the cup on the table, one of the oldest pieces of furniture she had in her home and one that had been with her through most of the ups and downs of her adult life. She felt each scratch, water stain, and imperfection represented a part of her. She was scratched, stained, and imperfect too. But she was still standing, sturdy and filled with purpose.

"Every woman of color brings beautiful richness of the diversity of gifts that God provides the church and reshapes the organization to make it more effective and relevant to the future of our church," Melissa said. "She can turn the conversation around and convince the board to reach into their church communities and find more diverse leadership."

Marilyn enthusiastically continued her friend's train of thought.

"Heart to Heart Sisters will do exactly that. It'll prepare multicultural women in the Lutheran church to become leaders within the church. Churches will then be able to better reach out to their communities—and to the world!"

Melissa rubbed her arms. "That just gave me chills."

Both women laughed.

"For so long the LWML was predominantly Anglo-Saxon women who wanted to reach out to other cultures but didn't know how to do so successfully. It has a history of standing up for the African American members, even cancelling the convention in 1955 when Black members were not allowed to stay in the hotel where the convention was to be held." Marilyn tapped her pen against the tablet she'd been writing on.

"Let's be honest, as well intended as I know all of the past and present leaders of LWML are, cultural barriers exist," Melissa said. "Hispanic women, more often than not, live in distinctly male-dominated homes. Cultural expectations are that women will not work outside the home, they'll be almost solely responsible for the children, and they'll take care of all domestic responsibilities like cooking and cleaning. A Hispanic woman would need approval from her husband to participate in the LWML. In some cases, that permission is granted; in others, it isn't. African and Asian cultures have similar beliefs. The Anglo-American culture is very different."

"So the ability to become part of Heart to Heart Sisters might be challenging for some women, depending on their individual cultural nuances," Marilyn said.

Melissa nodded. "Freedom to develop our God-given giftedness in service to the church and the world is a big deal. A program like Heart to Heart Sisters would not only help to diversify LWML culturally, but through it we could help women develop their inherent talents that they can bring to their churches and communities in whatever way works for them."

"In addition to helping women of color discover their talents, we could help them serve others through the LWML groups in their congregations or even through district or national committees." Marilyn turned the page in her notebook and scribbled in it again as she talked.

"Ideally, that would be wonderful," Melissa said. "Imagine— with a diversified organization, there would be changes in conversation that would lead to a broader vision."

She shook her head. "I'm still in awe. When I was a teen growing up near Compton listening to police helicopters circle my neighborhood almost every night, I would never have believed that one day the Lord would allow me to serve women who are often on the outside looking in. I have been blessed and privileged to be part of this. And I couldn't have chosen a better partner."

Marilyn pulled Melissa into a sisterly hug. "I couldn't have, either. God wrote us a specific plan and gently steered us along to this point."

"I'm certain God was leading and establishing this moment for his work and blessing for the LWML."

"Me too." Marilyn slid her notebook into her oversized handbag, which Melissa swore was the size of a beach tote that could also double as an overnight bag for a family of four.

After showing Marilyn to the door, Melissa plopped on the couch with a huge sigh. This new program would certainly alter the composition of the LWML. Hopefully, the organization was truly ready for the change.

Melissa thought of the description of Tabitha of Joppa in Acts 9: "This woman was abounding with deeds of kindness and charity which she continually did." The impact of the women who would be inspired to use their gifts, extend them to serve their sisters in Christ of all ethnicities and colors, and welcome them as full partners in the Gospel was immeasurable.

Melissa offered a prayer of thanksgiving.

"Jesus, we only wish to serve in those ways in which you intend. If Heart to Heart Sisters will help women of color serve LWML and embrace and share their own unique gifts, then please help our proposal to find favor. Let us secure interest, if it is your will."

Melissa at the Lutheran Hour Float, New Year's Day, Pasadena, Caifornia

With former Lutheran Hour Speaker Dr. Oswald Hoffman

***

Melissa wrapped up her speech at the district convention breakout session to energetic applause. The nods and interested looks she'd seen on the women's faces left her encouraged.

Marilyn and Melissa had been given speaking time along with a table where they could discuss the Heart to Heart Sisters program in more detail and distribute reading materials. They hoped to find women who could identify women of color within their churches who would benefit from Heart to Heart Sisters. They also planned to encourage women to help their sisters from ethnic congregations set up their own LWML groups and serve in ways that made sense for them.

"For you," Melissa said as she handed Marilyn a cup of coffee. She sat in the metal folding chair next to Marilyn.

"Have I told you lately that you're an angel?" Marilyn closed her eyes and took a long sip from the cup Melissa had given her.

"Yes, but I like to hear you say it again. And again." Melissa smirked and laughed out loud when Marilyn playfully punched her arm. Banter between the two women came easily.

"Excuse me. I was very impressed by your presentation." A friendly woman approached their table. Her badge read "Andrea," and she mentioned she was from a church in southern California.

Melissa greeted her enthusiastically. "Thank you so much. What can we tell you about Heart to Heart Sisters?"

"Well, I feel as if this program would be a great fit for my church, as we have an LCMS Sudanese congregation that worships in our church."

"Wonderful!" Marilyn said.

"How would we start?" Andrea asked.

"First, get to know some of the women in that congregation," Melissa explained. "Maybe visit their worship service. You will not understand their language, but what a great way to experience

Christine Schulden

what immigrant people experience every day as they make a new home in a new country."

Marilyn continued Melissa's train of thought. "There are always women who speak some English. Let them know about the LWML and how, as women of the LCMS, they are already a part of the organization. Let them know about its mission and how they can participate. Let them know they can form an LWML group in their own language."

"How exciting," Melissa interjected, elevating her voice, "would it be to see the LWML resemble the assembly in heaven where all nations and tribes, all races and languages, are there, as Revelation tells us in chapter seven, verse nine. I want to cry every time I think of this future and how we can strive for this reality in the present church."

Andrea nodded. "As a matter of fact, I do know someone from the Sudanese congregation. She is so knowledgeable about the Bible and dedicates so much time to prayer. When I hear her pray, I am in awe. She is clearly a leader to the women of her congregation."

"That's exactly who we're trying to reach through Heart to Heart Sisters," Melissa said.

Andrea patted the stack of information Marilyn had given her. "I'll reach out to her and tell her about this. Maybe it'll make a difference to her. Her gift would make a difference to many of us in the church."

"Please keep in touch with us. Our contact information is in the literature. If there's any way we can help, let us know."

"Thank you." Andrea moved along to another booth.

Marilyn turned to Melissa. "It's so encouraging to think of what women from different backgrounds can offer their churches once their talents have been cultivated."

Melissa nodded. "And maybe once we can get more diverse voices on the board, there'll be more impetus for women of color to come forward on their own and seek leadership roles."

Marilyn drained her coffee cup. "You've got a point there, my friend. In the meantime, let's be patient and watch God work."

Chapter 16

M elissa continued to spend her days working with Heart to Heart Sisters, helping Concordia Chula Vista plant a mission church on the U.S. side near the border, and traveling to Tijuana to ensure the outreach she'd started there was still running smoothly. To say she was exhausted was an understatement. But her desire to serve God and her love for people and ministry on both sides of the border kept her going, and she was always thinking of new ways to connect with the diverse women of the church and the LWML.

Women from various cultural groups were invited to LWML conventions and served in leadership roles during Heart to Heart Sisters training and sharing sessions. During meetings the Heart to Heart Sisters committee also led district presidents in Bafá Bafá, a cross-cultural game in which participants were assigned invented cultures with both written and unwritten "rules." They tried to decipher other participants' facial cues according to how their own culture would react, but, of course, the rules were not the same. Afterward, when Marilyn and Melissa would debrief the participants, their faces would light up with understanding. "Oh, that was a cultural misunderstanding," they would say. "We can see how frustrating that can be."

Many women who'd received training through Heart to Heart were now serving in their districts and churches. One of the bright and inspirational women who'd gone through the program had recently become a district president. Diversification of LWML was increasing, from grassroots churches up to the executive committee of LWML itself.

"Did that situation in New Mexico work out?" Marilyn turned to Melissa as the women worked one day. "The one where a congregant interested in LWML went to a meeting with her child and was told they didn't have childcare for the meeting?"

Melissa shook her head. "Yes, I still can't get over that. This is exactly why we are trying to help women better understand other cultures."

"I know." Marilyn sighed. "The story that Evelyn told us still haunts me. How uncomfortable she felt when she went to a meeting at her church and she was the only woman of color there. She said that while the women seemed welcoming, it was still uncomfortable for her because there was nothing that spoke to her directly and nothing that welcomed her culturally."

"I'm happy to say that in many situations, change has happened with the learning that Heart to Heart has offered. The Lord has done so much, Marilyn. There are women of many cultures serving in our organization and even many who have been asked to serve on our Synod's boards and commissions. Having a place at the table with their unique perspective is so important. Women whose gifts and talents have been cultivated are now expanding the organization's worldview. They're adding new levels of consideration to the decisions and thought processes of the church at large. It's astounding."

"As of now, over two hundred women have passed through the Heart to Heart Sisters program and have connected in different levels of the organization," Marilyn pointed out. "And we're only just beginning."

"Many other women are bound to see how their cultures are embraced by the Lutheran church—how their voices can and will be heard," Melissa said. "I've no doubt that this will draw other women into leadership roles."

Marilyn's fingers flew over the keyboard. "Here's how the new *Lutheran Woman's Quarterly* looks." She turned the laptop around so Melissa could see the magazine's online edition.

Out of the blue, the editor had contacted Melissa to let her know there was a page that couldn't be used for ad space and had asked if Heart to Heart Sisters would like to fill the page by translating a Bible study into Spanish for each issue.

"I can't believe it," Melissa brought a hand to her mouth and fought back tears. "Look at how beautiful the Bible verses are. They're all in Spanish. The layout is gorgeous!"

"So many women will feel even more a part of LWML now that they're being spoken to directly in their first language. Having content in a language other than English communicates what is important to us."

Heart to Heart Sisters itself had also been featured in a recent LWML magazine, and donations and inquiries had begun to flow in as a result. The future of the program was bright.

Chapter 17

"Your prayers have been answered," Tere said, swooping into Melissa's office. The Tijuana heat was insufferable, and Melissa's fan did nothing but blow around the hot air.

Melissa wiped her face with a paper towel. "A truck full of ice is coming that I can jump into?"

Tere rolled her eyes. "Close, but if you can believe it, it's even better than that."

"Now you've piqued my interest." Melissa clasped her hands, making a steeple out of her two index fingers.

"That group from Omaha that contacted you? They'll be here tomorrow."

"Wow. OK, then." Melissa looked around the office space, once sparse with only a desk and bottled water station but now full of furniture, color, and life.

"Dick Rockenbach is bringing a group with him, and he was hoping to shadow us to get an idea of what we do here."

"Is he planning on staying for a month? We do a lot of different things here, and we need help with all of them."

Tere laughed. "I'm sure you'll show him everything possible."

Now that Heart to Heart Sisters had become a success and was running on its own merit, Melissa had begun calling around to conferences, women's groups, and churches in an effort to find events where she could speak about the Tijuana outreach. She had been fortunate to receive many invitations to speak, and those had resulted in unexpected, kind donations to benefit the program. When she was invited to speak to a team from Messiah Lutheran Church in Nebraska led by Dick and Sue Rockenbach, she knew she'd found an organization that had much in common with her own.

Much like the Tijuana outreach program, the team's goal was to coordinate projects among churches, families, and communities in order to improve the quality of life for those in need. Melissa recalled her lengthy conversations with Dick over countless appetizers and cups of coffee. He'd embraced her passion for the people of Tijuana and had told her that he'd eventually lead a team to Tijuana to see how his organization could improve the community Melissa had been working with. She just didn't think it would happen so quickly.

"I know that you and some of the other volunteers can help me." Melissa flipped open her planner to the page she'd tagged with a paper clip.

Melissa and her crew of volunteers had seen the community's immense spiritual growth as a result of the Bible studies and the other religious education they'd provided for both children and adults. But one thing they were missing was a church—and a pastor to lead and teach. Melissa had been asked to submit a proposal to receive a door offering at the national LWML convention to fund a bivocational pastor—a pastor who would serve the church in addition to working another job.

Tere plopped in the chair across from Melissa and wiped off her glistening brow. "It would mean so much to get a pastor here. A pastor to minister to and baptize people in Tijuana would be an immeasurable blessing. Could you imagine the community's joy? We began by aiding them with their physical health, and now we're helping them with their spiritual health. And my sons can grow up with a strong faith. What other miracle is God going to work down here? I'm beginning to believe that you don't ever sleep. I don't know when you find the time, bouncing between your home near San Diego, working with Concordia Church and the LWML, and driving over the border multiple times per week to help us out down here."

"All of these missions are important to me, and so many others count on them," Melissa said. "But I've learned to seek help these past several years. I have people like you who know how to handle everything when I can't be present. It's truly a blessing to have people in a position to help and do the job as well as I can."

Tere blushed, and Melissa knew she was looking at the future director of the Tijuana ministry. "I'm honored you feel that way. While I may be competent, there's no way I can fill your shoes."

The door to the office opened. An older woman and a young woman with an infant wrapped in her arms entered. Both women had harsh lines that creased their brows, deeply bronzed skin, dust-covered threadbare skirts, and well-worn sandals. Melissa hurried over to the water dispenser and filled two cups, offering one to each woman.

"Please have a seat." Melissa sat in the chair at her desk and motioned for the women to take the seats across from her. They looked at each other, and when the older one nodded, the two sat down carefully. Each took a sip of the water. After the first taste, the younger woman eagerly drank the rest.

"How can we help you today?" Melissa leaned her elbows on her desk. She'd noted their worn clothing when they'd walked in, but now she noticed their chapped hands and the peeling skin on their cheeks and noses. These women worked hard, perhaps in the fields gathering vegetables. If that were the case, their wages were hardly enough to scrape by.

The baby let out a thin, reedy cry. The young woman pressed the child closer to her breast while gently bouncing her arms up and down. The sounds the child had made didn't seem quite right, and Melissa wondered if the mother or baby had received proper medical attention during and after the pregnancy.

"How old is your baby?"

"Josés three months old," the older woman said, the creases on her forehead deepening as the child cried out weakly.

"Congratulations," Tere said with a smile. But neither the young mother nor the older woman smiled back.

"Our life hasn't been easy." The older woman pressed a fist to her mouth and took a few deep breaths before continuing. "My husband passed away unexpectedly two years ago, leaving us with no money. My daughter and I had no skills, so we had no choice but to work in the fields. In the evenings, we took jobs sewing when they were available. Anita met someone in the fields, and they married young. She hoped her husband could provide us with some financial stability, but soon after they got married, he left for a job in the United States. He told us it was temporary. We haven't heard from him since. We don't even know if that's really where he went. He never sent us money like he promised. But he left us with José."

Melissa's heart ached. Sadly, this story was all too common. Women in Mexico without vocational skills had few ways to support themselves and their children.

"All we want is to make sure José gets a better life than what we can give him now." The young mother looked at her child as if he were the most beautiful thing in the world.

"We need skills. Someone told us you can help us to learn how to read." José's grandmother stared at Melissa.

"We have many ways that we can help," Melissa said. "We don't currently have a literacy program."

"But we can teach you how to read," Tere interjected, "through our youth program and our Bible study program."

Melissa was encouraged by Tere's comment. While a literacy program had been something they'd been considering, participants in Bible study and youth outreach had been learning to read and write by absorbing what they were being taught. Getting these women involved would go a long way to improving their lives.

"Do you have birth certificates? For yourselves or for José?" Melissa knew that for any child in Mexico to receive a public education, a birth certificate was a must. And if this child had been born at home and neither his mother nor his grandmother was literate, the chance of them knowing how to apply for a birth certificate for him was scant.

"No." Jo's mother avoided eye contact with Melissa as she fussed with her son's blanket. "None of us going back five generations have birth certificates. We didn't go to school, either."

"Well, that's not a problem. Through our program you'll learn how to read, and we can help you with the process to get a birth certificate. Rest assured; José will be eligible to receive a good education." Tere started to give them a list of upcoming programs but quickly realized her mistake. "Be at the community center tomorrow at four o'clock. Our friendship meeting will be held first, with the Bible study after. Can you make it?"

The young mother nodded, but her mother pursed her lips. "One of us has to work to keep food on our table."

"I understand," Melissa said. "We're happy you found us, and we're glad to help."

A Mexican woman's pride could prevent her from accepting what she'd consider a handout, so it wasn't often that a woman like José's grandmother would seek the help of an outreach program. But in this case, she and her family were being given a chance to help themselves by becoming educated. This was much different from a handout; rather, it was a "hand up," a way of providing someone with something to make their life better.

Melissa knew there was yet another facet of this program that needed to take root: a way to give people skills and opportunities to better their lives. Physical and spiritual health were important, of course, but so was skill development, so children might expect a better future than their parents had. Melissa would make sure that would happen. But how?

Chapter 18

Melissa closed her eyes and listened to the hum of the refrigerator, the tap-tapping of the hammer, and the laughter and chatter of the crew. The fumes of fresh paint mixed with the scent of the oil that had been rubbed into the new oak flooring.

Dick Rockenbach wiped his hands on his pants as he excitedly strode toward Melissa. "We're almost done. Just a little more work on the trim and some touching up here and there. I'd say by this weekend you'll be all set to start the breakfast program."

The group from Messiah Lutheran had come to Tijuana to refurbish a little brick building that would be used for Sunday school and children's programs, including a breakfast initiative. They'd installed flooring and a kitchen in the attached parsonage, helped run the revamped youth program, and attended friendship meetings and Bible studies. During the week, Melissa had spoken to Dick about hiring a full-time pastor but had lamented the small, abandoned building that would have to pass for a parsonage. With limited funding, Melissa couldn't see how the place could be made habitable, much less the site for the breakfast program she'd been hoping to start.

Within weeks after he'd returned to Nebraska, Dick called Melissa.

"When do you think we could come back? I have a team all prepared to do some repairs to that parsonage and to build the kitchen you were hoping for. And then we can finish up the flooring and the altar in the little church building to make it ready for worship."

Melissa looked at the phone receiver in disbelief. Surely she'd misheard him.

"But we don't have the funding for that yet. I'm working on some fundraising ideas, but our donors have been taxed lately with all of the contributions we've asked for. I need a little more time to be able to pay for the labor and the materials."

"Oh, Melissa. That's what I love so much about you. You're always so pragmatic. And you never expect anything from anyone. Messiah Lutheran Church and its partners in ministry is providing everything for this project: the materials, the labor, and the transportation. All you'll need to do is find some locals who are willing to give us a hand and then sit back and watch the transformation."

And what a transformation it was. The parsonage now had a sprawling kitchen with a large refrigerator and huge stove. The counters seemed limitless. There was space for at least two picnic tables. Overhead lighting and ceiling fans finished off the room.

With some of the leftover materials, the group had refurbished the family room, which would double as the pastor's office, as well as a small bedroom. They'd also modernized the plumbing, added a bathroom, and painted the house inside and out. One of the most special moments had come when little Iván Andres, Tere's youngest son, was baptized after a workday. Dick and Sue Rockenbach, still covered in dust and dirt and sweat stains, served as godparents, and the tears flowed as the group experienced the miracle of seeing a child enter the family of God.

"This weekend we can begin serving breakfast to the community." Melissa could hardly believe the generosity of the Nebraska congregation.

A slim man dressed in black entered the kitchen, wiping his brow. His eyes widened at the nearly complete kitchen.

"I can't believe this." He turned in a slow circle, taking in everything.

"Isn't it exactly what we'd been praying for, Job?"

Job Jiménez was the bi-vocational pastor who had been chosen to minister to the people supported by the Tijuana outreach program. Melissa's proposal had not only been accepted by the LWML, but it had also received a door offering of $32,000 from the recent LWML convention in Albuquerque.

Job shook his head, tears gleaming in his eyes. "When I was a young man in the seminary in Argentina, I felt drawn back to Mexico. I'm from the border region of Mexico, and somehow I knew my calling was here. But when I was first offered the opportunity to be pastor here, and when I first visited, I will admit, like the Apostle Thomas, I had my doubts. But now, thanks to Messiah Lutheran's ministry and the LWML, God has seen it fit to give me a ministry in Tijuana."

Now that the parsonage had been upgraded and a functional kitchen had been installed, the breakfast program could begin. And Job, who had a degree as a psychologist, could run a youth program that would not only provide spiritual guidance to at-risk youth, but also help them with self-esteem issues and addictions.

The community center had been spruced up, too, through the kindness of a former chemistry professor whose team visited Melissa yearly. The previous year, she and her team had built a shade structure so the children could have Sunday school lessons outside.

Melissa slid behind the wheel of her car, reflecting on the Tijuana outreach as she drove across the border. The volunteer pool kept growing, and the donations were coming in steadily enough that Melissa had been able to create a budget to support the programs that ran regularly. And now a pastor had been assigned to the church.

God had established the Tijuana ministry with few resources and many collaborators. How beautiful it was, Melissa thought, to see many give some and some give a lot to ensure people in Tijuana would have a ministry where their families could connect, learn, and grow.

Everything was perfect—until it no longer was.

Chapter 19

2011

Melissa couldn't stop the tears from forming; she just hoped they wouldn't fall. To cry in front of the regional supervisor and the director of Lutheran Hour Ministries (LHM) and the area counselor of Latin America would be wholly unprofessional. But after fourteen years of cultivating the program in Tijuana, doing independent fundraising on behalf of the mission, investing in the community, and making close contacts in the local government, Melissa thought her ministry had demonstrated that Tijuana was a place of great opportunity and faithfulness for the Gospel and should have received greater consideration.

"Of course, we're offering you a severance package," said Alex Schmidt, the LHM director. Alex grimaced as he pushed the envelope across the table.

Melissa put down her fork next to her salad plate. A severance package meant nothing to her when the people she'd been helping for so long would now suddenly be without the support they'd come to rely on. She stuck the envelope in her purse without looking at it.

Alex cleared his throat. Melissa bit her tongue to prevent herself from saying what she really wanted to. You could see the pain in his eyes. He knew how hard this would be on Melissa and the ministry. She suspected that Alex and regional supervisor Dan

Williams had opted to break the news to Melissa at a trendy St. Louis restaurant to make an uncomfortable and heartbreaking moment more palatable, and maybe melt into light conversation and the noise of a busy eatery.

Alex wiped his mouth with the starchy, white napkin he'd tucked into the collar of his shirt.

"I'm sure you understand our decision to move the outreach office from Tijuana has nothing to do with the job you've done. Your work has touched many lives for which we are truly thankful."

"Thank you for saying that, but I can't understand why you're making this change after fourteen years." Melissa pushed her plate away. She'd hardly touched it since her stomach soured after she'd been told that LHM would no longer support the outreach in Tijuana and that the entire ministry was being uprooted and moved to Mexico City.

"Melissa, the office must work more collaboratively with our sister church in Mexico, and Mexico City is where they are located. The work on the border, nearly two thousand miles away, has largely been left to grow on its own. This distance has caused tension and hurt feelings for nearly eighty years."

"But what about the opportunities in this fast-growing region of Mexico where hearts are open and people are seeking God in ways they don't when they are in the interior of the country?" Melissa clenched the napkin in her lap. She didn't want her lunch companions to see her frustration. Plus, she knew they were only trying to steward LHM resources wisely.

"While community support is wonderful, it's only part of what our international ministries program does," Dan tried to explain.. "We work where there is a strong sister church presence and established churches to which people can be referred. Maybe someday that will be the case in Tijuana, but it is not true now."

Alex flicked his tie over his shoulder and tucked his napkin back into his collar. "We only have so many resources. In order to ensure that we are successful, we can't spread them too thin."

"In Tijuana, we have ensured that we work toward self-funding and lean on LHM for fewer and fewer resources all the time." Melissa felt her chin tremble.

"And we appreciate that. But to work more closely with our Mexican Lutheran partners we have to allocate all of the resources that have been used in Tijuana to Mexico City." Dan leaned back in his seat, hoping Melissa would understand. .

Melissa couldn't understand how either one of these men could have an appetite when they were pulling the plug on thriving, growing, and fruitful work.

"We ultimately would like to build this arm in Mexico City into something bigger," Dan continued. "A partnership in Mexico City could splinter off into many ministries and reach more people than we can now."

"Is there any way that the LHM would consider keeping the offices in Tijuana open, even if just part time?"

"It's too much of a stretch." Dan dropped his napkin on the table.

"What if I cut my salary in half?"

"Melissa, we aren't paying you all that much to begin with. You've already taken a minimal salary." Alex handed over his glass when the waitress offered him more water.

The clinking of the ice cubes and the condensation that dripped from the cold pitcher of water made Melissa think of the sweltering heat that those in Tijuana endured day in and out. She thought of how the small fan in her office did little to provide relief and how so many people there didn't even have the means to have electricity to run a refrigerator that would provide them with ice.

"We appreciate what you've done on behalf of the ministry for the benefit of our international missions. We have the building for two more weeks. After that, it needs to be shut down."

"But what if . . ." Melissa raised a hand, a new idea popping into her head.

"I'm sorry Melissa, our decision is final," Dan said firmly.

Melissa clamped her mouth shut before she said something inappropriate. While she didn't agree with this decision, she still had great respect for the LHM and the work she was doing with them through the LWML. She understood that resources were finite and that the LHM was doing its best to support many ministries across the globe. But while she knew this decision wasn't personal, she also knew she couldn't allow her mission in Tijuana to end in this way.

Her lunch with Alex and Dan ended courteously even though Melissa felt sour inside. At the airport, she flopped into a seat and flicked sullenly through a magazine she'd picked up to pass the time during her layover. She'd wanted to get home as quickly as possible, but the flight the LHM had booked for her had a layover in Denver.

"Excuse me. Is this seat taken?" Melissa looked into the kind face of a man who was about twenty years her senior. His soft eyes held her attention.

"It's not. Please, have a seat."

"Thank you. I have a layover, and it's not supposed to be for too long, so I thought coming to the gate right away was a smart decision. Apparently, everyone else traveling to Los Angeles thought so too."

"Where are you coming from?" Melissa set her magazine aside.

"St. Louis."

"Me too!" It was then that Melissa noticed he wore a clerical collar. "You're a pastor?"

119

"Yes, I'm a Lutheran pastor," he good-naturedly explained. "I'm a counselor in the LCMS Pacific Southwest District. I'm returning home from a visit to our Synod offices in St. Louis."

"So am I." Melissa couldn't help but chuckle at the surprised look on the pastor's face. "Well, what a beautiful coincidence!"

Melissa chuckled. "You never know who you'll bump into, do you?"

"Our good Lord works in mysterious ways. Why were you in St. Louis?"

"A ministry office of Lutheran Hour Ministries I lead in Tijuana is being shut down and moved to Mexico City. After fourteen years!"

"I'm sorry to hear that. It must have been quite a blow to you." The pastor took off his glasses and cleaned them with a cloth he'd pulled from an inner pocket of his jacket. "Tell me about your mission."

Melissa talked about everything the last fourteen years had brought to the people of Tijuana. She spoke of the programs and the pastor who'd been recently placed there—all of the unique things she and others had contributed to open doors for the Gospel and revive hope among people who often were hopeless amid daily crime and poverty. She spoke of how residents had learned to rely on each other for support.

The pastor rubbed his chin with his index finger and thumb. "You're a resilient woman. And a resourceful one. While this might seem like a blow to your ministry in Tijuana, I feel as if this might be an opportunity for you instead."

"I'm sorry, Pastor. I fail to see how." Melissa shook her head, her eyes filling with tears.

"I know you feel orphaned right now, but you know LHM doesn't take any of its work lightly. Each ministry is important to them. They had a difficult choice to make and chose to move on because they felt this choice would open up the opportunity to reach even more people. But you said yourself that you self-funded most of the needs of the mission through the contacts you'd made. So why not reach out to them? Explain what happened, and find a way to keep the mission active, but independently."

On the plane, Melissa buckled herself into her seat and tapped her fingers on her knee, deep in thought. She pulled the envelope containing her severance offer from her purse and dug for a pen. A rush of ideas flowed from her head onto the envelope. The more she wrote, the more determined she became. She promised herself she'd do everything in her power to save her ministry in Tijuana. There was no way Melissa would abandon those people, especially not when they still needed support.

"Jesus," Melissa prayed. "You have planted us on the border for your purposes and the blessing of many of your beloved children. You have allowed us to develop trust among people in many communities, as well as built a network that supports the work here. Now that LHM is taking on a new direction, make that work fruitful and help us continue the work that you have called us to do. Help us find ways to seek, bless, serve, and encourage the people you have given to us throughout Tijuana. We trust you and know your resources are never-ending. Provide from your storehouses, Lord. Amen."

Melissa opened the front door to her home and dropped her keys and purse on a bench in the foyer. She slipped off her jacket and hung it haphazardly in the coat closet, then pulled a can of coffee from the kitchen cabinet. Once the machine beeped, she poured some into her favorite—and largest—mug, adding her preferred amount of sugar and cream. Then she curled up on the couch and opened her Bible.

Melissa knew life was full of curveballs. The only way she could successfully navigate any setback or struggle was to find comfort in knowing that the Lord was with her to guide her through. His plan for her was clear, but she'd have to hurdle the obstacles that unpredictably landed in the way.

She turned to James 1, verses 2-4, and read: "Consider it pure joy, my brothers and sisters, whenever you face trials of many kinds, because you know that the testing of your faith produces perseverance. Let perseverance finish its work so that you may be mature and compete, not lacking anything."

She continued reading and found that verse 12 also applied to the struggle that currently overwhelmed her: "Blessed is the one who perseveres under trial because, having stood the test, that person will receive the crown of life that the Lord has promised to those who love him."

And love the Lord she did. Melissa had a small team, but her volunteers were giant in their faith and confident that the Lord would provide. She was always inspired by their commitment and complete trust in God. She wouldn't face the unknown road ahead alone. She knew God would make a way for her team to carry on the work in Tijuana.

Chapter 20

2012

"So I am asking if we, as the community of Concordia Chula Vista, would embrace the special people of Tijuana and sponsor this ministry." Melissa pulled the microphone attached to the lectern a little closer, fearing the congregation could not hear her. Despite the fact that she was speaking directly to the congregants in her own church, a solid knot was tied in her belly. She had put a lot of faith into her church community, praying that asking them to take the place of the LHM as the umbrella organization for the Tijuana ministry would be met with approval. During the many years she'd attended Concordia, its members had always been so generous to the Tijuana ministry; she hoped they would continue their support.

"We are asking for one percent of the weekly offerings for operational costs. In addition, we'll invite donors from the greater church to support this work too. We'll sponsor mission trips so that people can experience how the local team in Tijuana serves people in need and brings them the hope found in Jesus." Melissa looked around at the congregants, most of whom were paying close attention. The knot in her belly loosened just a little.

"I promise once you visibly see the good works that are being done there, you'll understand the full scope of this mission, and you'll be proud to support it." Melissa saw some people nod.

"We call this mission 'One Thousand Generations.' God's promise to us is to be there for all of us through our life and into our eternal rest. And with One Thousand Generations, we make that same promise to those in Tijuana. We know that hope in Jesus will impact future generations."

Melissa wrapped up her speech to a smattering of applause. After the service she made her way to the small area at the back of the church where people would often gather over light refreshments and coffee. She expected some congregants might have questions, and she wanted to be present to answer them and address any concerns.

"I'm impressed with the work you're doing internationally. It's important to take care of our neighbors, especially those who are so close!" A petite woman with dark black hair said to Melissa as she ran her finger along the rim of her coffee cup.

"Thank you." Melissa found herself smiling at the woman, noting her sincerity. "I've found that what affects the people of Tijuana the most is hopelessness in their life experience. That includes poverty, violence, crime, and too few opportunities to have an education. They don't often see a way out or a way forward for their children to have a better life. Many people suffer from illiteracy and few opportunities for work that can support their families. A factory position may include a six-day work week, ten hours a day—and for $50 a week. Often families must help each other out by sharing a makeshift shelter to cover childcare, daily living expenses, and food."

Soon others joined in the conversation, all with words of encouragement and promises of help. Many expressed interest in traveling to Tijuana, excited to aid the mission.

"Not bad today, Melissa." Richard Schmidt, the pastor, placed a hand on her shoulder after most of the crowd had cleared. "As if I had any doubts you'd win them over."

"I was hoping that would be the case," Melissa admitted. "Did you hear much from people who are unwilling to sponsor One Thousand Generations? Did anyone feel imposed upon by the idea of taking one percent from the church and donating it to the mission?"

Pastor Schmidt shook his head. "To the contrary. People were asking what they could do to help even beyond the donations."

Melissa blew out a sigh of relief. "I'm so happy to hear that."

"We're happy to support this mission in any way we can. It's a privilege to serve our nearest neighbors to the south."

***

One Thousand Generations had been set up under the umbrella of Concordia so that donors could support the ministry in Tijuana and still receive tax receipts for their donations in the United States.

One percent of the Concordia budget was awarded to the ministry in Tijuana; the outreach also received contributions from about two dozen supporters. This funding covered only the essentials—utilities, expenses for the community center that housed the office, a stipend for the mission team, and outreach programs and supplies. Melissa needed to figure out another source of funds. Grassroots efforts were a must.

***

Dozens of colorful, intricate piñatas lined tables in the community center. Tere and Melissa had brought a team of single mothers together to make these beautiful creations for the women to sell in the open-air markets of Tijuana. Locals and tourists bought the perfectly crafted souvenirs that supported both the crafters and One Thousand Generations.

Through generous donations and these women's own scrap piles, the key materials to make the piñatas had all been provided: glue, cardboard, crepe paper, and balloons. Pencils for drawing the shape of the piñatas on cardboard, scissors for cutting them out, and strips of crepe paper in a rainbow of colors had been neatly set out, creating an assembly line for the women to work on their creations.

The women's chatter warmed Melissa's heart. So many had seemed broken when she'd first met them, all with their own stories of grief and desperation. Some had found themselves pregnant unexpectedly; others had spouses who had died or were killed in the more dangerous parts of the city. Still others had partners who had abandoned their children, which had left the mothers destitute. Many of these single mothers didn't have other family members they could turn to for help. Some had scavenged the streets for food and shelter for themselves and their children. The majority of these women had little education and lacked the skills to get jobs that could support them. Through One Thousand Generations, these women had found support and a way to learn practical skills so they could earn money and get on their feet.

As the women worked, their children were cared for in the sheltered area near the parsonage. While there, the children dug into Scripture to learn about Jesus, sang songs of worship, and created arts and crafts that reinforced the day's message and helped the lessons stick in their minds. Knowing their children were safe enabled the mothers to relax, enjoy each other, and experience the love of God in a special way that put them on a path to living a life of faith.

Melissa could visibly see the changes in many of these women. She'd always told her team of volunteers that a woman can often tell what the life of another woman is like just by looking at her, regardless of economic or cultural differences. When Melissa had first told Tere this, she had laughed.

"Oh, Melissa, that might be true in California, but Mexico is different."

"When you see a young woman who has visible signs of fatigue around her eyes yet has a serenity about her, what do you know about her?" Melissa asked, using a pair of scissors to cut the outline of a donkey from the sheet of cardboard in front of her.

"I'd assume she's a new mother with a newborn baby."

"And why would you think that?"

"The serenity. All new mothers wear that look of love." Tere stopped talking and laughed. "OK, OK. You're right, Melissa. I see what you're talking about."

"And that look is the same whether you're Hispanic, white, or African American, and whether you're from Mexico or California or even Sweden. A mother knows another mother. A woman knows another woman."

"And these women?" Tere glanced at the group of women laughing, gluing, singing, and cutting. Colorful strips of crepe paper clung to their clothes, their hands covered in paste.

"These women are survivors. They've survived more than many of us have, and through that survival, they can teach the rest of us how to do it when our time comes." Melissa set the scissors down and picked up a stack of newspapers. She began to cut the paper into strips for the women to dip into the paste and form into the shapes they wanted for their piñatas.

"We all have our stories of survival, that's for sure." Tere picked up her own scissors and started cutting the newspaper in front of her. "Women are often hard on each other, but from my experiences, when they see another woman suffering, they're quick to come to one another's aid."

Melissa knew Tere was right—as usual.

***

A black and white image of Jacobeth lying in her bed, her watery eyes and deep facial creases belying her pain and sadness, filled the presentation screen behind Melissa.

"Jacobeth is eighty-one years old. She suffers from hypertension and diabetes and has been bedridden for years due to a fractured hip that hasn't healed properly." Melissa folded her hands and placed them on the podium. She didn't need notes to share about the people of Tijuana with those who'd gathered at the LWML meeting to which she'd been invited. Melissa had seen their suffering firsthand. She'd been in the field nurturing them and feeding them spiritually, emotionally, and physically. She could tell their stories as easily as she could tell her own. The people of Tijuana were a part of her now.

"While she's fortunate enough to have her children to care for her, she can't go to church. One Thousand Generations makes sure that Jacobeth's spiritual health is cared for by bringing God to her through phone calls or visitation and by reading the Bible with her."

Melissa clicked her mouse, and the image changed from the picture of Jacobeth to a photo of about a dozen children of all ages.

"This property houses five full families. It's located in one of the most dangerous areas of Tijuana—the part of the city that averages three murders per week." Melissa grimaced. That statistic always gnawed at her heart.

"Parents are afraid to leave their children to go to work. They are unable to attend church or allow their children to go to Sunday school out of fear for their lives. One Thousand Generations visits these families regularly and provides them with catechism materials as well as hygiene kits and vitamins."

Melissa moved to the next slide, which contained a black and white photo of a beautiful, middle-aged woman whose long black hair was pulled back in a ponytail.

"Ester called one of our longest-serving volunteers early in the morning one day. She told Tere that her twenty-three-year-old son, who'd defied all odds and was finishing his last year at university, had been missing for twenty-four hours. A couple of hours later

Tere received a text from Ester that read only, 'They killed my son.' After hours of unsuccessfully trying to reach Ester, Tere finally got a return call."

Melissa paused and wiped a tear from her eye.

"Tijuana is wrought with poverty. Those who are stricken the most become emboldened to take whatever they can in whatever way is necessary in order to survive. Ester's son had been robbed and murdered for what little he had in his pockets. Those who killed him didn't know that he'd come from the same level of poverty they were suffering in. They didn't know he was a bright star who supported his family at a young age after his father abandoned the family. He worked two jobs and studied diligently, finishing up a professional degree. He was the apple of his mother's eye.

"One Thousand Generations supported Ester spiritually by praying with her and for her. We stood by her during her son's funeral and extended to her the love she needs during this most difficult time."

Melissa moved to the front of the podium to address her audience in a more intimate way.

"One Thousand Generations is more than just a charity. It offers support in ways that are unique to the person that needs help. We have become a trusted part of the community, a place that people can come to knowing they'll be offered the hand up that they need in their time of crisis or even in their daily lives. We strive through our teachings to provide the type of love and compassion that extends beyond this generation and into the many generations beyond, all based in the words of our Lord, Jesus Christ."

Melissa paused and looked around. The sorrow she saw on some of the women's faces let her know she was getting through to them and that the real stories she'd brought from the field were making their mark on their hearts.

"We turn to Psalm 90, which to us seems to speak about One Thousand Generations and what we hope to accomplish in the name of Jesus Christ." Melissa cleared her throat before reciting to the crowd.

"Lord, you have been our dwelling place throughout all generations. Before the mountains were born or you brought forth the whole world, from everlasting to everlasting you are God. You turn people back to dust, saying, 'Return to dust, you mortals.' A thousand years in your sight are like a day that has just gone by, or like a watch in the night. Yet you sweep people away in the sleep of death—they are like the new grass of the morning: In the morning it springs up new, but by evening it is dry and withered."

Melissa closed her eyes, then picked up at verse 14.

"Satisfy us in the morning with your unfailing love, that we may sing for joy and be glad all our days. Make us glad for as many days as you have afflicted us, for as many years as we have seen trouble. May your deeds be shown to your servants, your splendor to their children. May the favor of the Lord our God rest on us; establish the work of our hands for us—yes, establish the work of our hands."

Melissa clicked off the presentation. "May the Lord bless you all."

She stepped off the platform to the floor, moving into the wings as the women began to filter from the meeting room where she'd been speaking. The messages she received from those who stopped to speak with her filled her heart with joy.

"Our church would like to provide you with support, if you'd accept," offered one woman.

"I'm from Mexico. It wasn't until I saw your message today that I truly understood the scope of your mission," another woman told her.

"What other projects does your ministry sponsor? How can we help?" someone else asked.

Melissa was overwhelmed with gratitude. One Thousand Generations ran on a lean budget. Large donations were possible and certainly appreciated, but the number of sizeable gifts varied from year to year. What was much more viable was a steady trickle of small donations. Melissa knew that at this gathering she'd not only found the sustainable donors she'd been seeking, but she'd also impacted the women of the LWML in a way they'd not been touched before. They now could see firsthand the impact of her outreach in Tijuana as well as the missions that other women served elsewhere.

Melissa knew one thing was still missing that would make the mission complete: collaboration. Was it possible? She had to find out.

Chapter 21
Tijuana, Mexico | 2019

Melissa sat across from David Gonzalez, president of the Lutheran Synod of Mexico (LSM). It was a regular Monday afternoon, and this was a surprise visit. Rev. Gonzalez was supportive of border ministries since he himself came from a border town. His approach to workers is kind and he is always looking for ways to support ministries and forge new ministry friendships.

Her mind raced as she tried to put together her ideas about border ministry without any preparation. But she was happy to explore what a partnership might mean and how One Thousand Generations could bless the Mexican Synod. One Thousand Generations was always looking for ways to support the new work happening in Mexico. The new pastoral formation program and deaconess program established by the Lutheran Synod of Mexico was the most exciting new ministry in years. Even Tere had enrolled in the maiden program for deaconess formation. Tere was helping edit materials and assisted coordinating satellite training sessions.

Melissa, her hands folded in front of her as if in prayer, tried to understand where this conversation was going. "As time has passed, I'm sure we've both seen the needs of the Mexican people grow "she said. President Gonzalez agreed. He was smiling, but still, Melissa held her coffee cup tightly, her knuckles white. Her stomach was in knots, and she felt her brow break into a sweat. She knew this meeting was long overdue. Then President Gonzalez spoke.

"We can work together to establish new ministries and train workers. The workers in the field say their number one need is theological training and support. We need pastors, deaconesses, and trained Sunday school teachers and evangelists. How can we work together to bring the right people and resources together to give Mexico the workers it needs for ministry in this new generation?"

Melissa's heart skipped a beat. This was more than she'd anticipated saying, but she went on.

"Border ministries have so much capacity to grow because of the incredible growth and migration of people from the south to the northern border. Far from their villages and extended family, they have an opportunity to explore a relationship with the living God as he has revealed himself in Scripture. There is spiritual need, and trained workers are needed to teach, guide, and care for people who face so many challenges and dangers in this border region.

"I think bi-vocational ministry will be key in Mexico," she continued. "We have tried to emulate an American model of a congregation that supports its pastor. In Mexico, we have concentrated our mercy work in the outlying areas of cities such as Tijuana. These communities are poor, and they move often in search of work. A bi-vocational model for workers can lend stability to ministry and makes the involvement of lay workers absolutely necessary. That is a good thing. In fact, I think bi-vocational ministry is an important model for the American church of the future. So let's be on the forefront here in Tijuana!"

"Let's keep this conversation going," David said as he stood up and shook Melissa's hand. The discussion to explore the possibilities of collaborative effort between the Tijuana ministry and the LSM in Mexico had begun. Despite a distance of nearly two thousand miles, Melissa was convinced this conversation had to continue. She was committed to keeping those lines of communication open for the blessing and benefit of the work the Lord wanted to see happen in the beautiful country of Mexico.

Melissa soon received another piece of good news: Her brother, Mark, had been rescued from his long struggle with drugs. Melissa's family had been praying daily for 18 years that God would make himself known to Mark in a real way, and not only had he met a woman of faith and become active in a church in Pennsylvania, he was now receiving opportunities to talk to young people about how God never gives up on his people.

***

"I can't thank you enough. We've raised over $4,000 as a result of your efforts and your kindness." Melissa shook the hands of Luther and Londa Skov, two patrons of One Thousand Generations who generously sewed and sold quilts to support the Tijuana ministry. The Skovs also coordinated quilt-making efforts among women in their church, including one who was ninety-five years old. The women worked diligently to produce beautiful pieces, some of which took more than a hundred hours to craft, and then would either donate the quilts or sell them through One Thousand Generations' social media channels.

"It's our pleasure to support the women of Tijuana," Londa said. She and her husband had just presented the pastor of the church and his new wife with a white, purple, and lavender quilt.

"The talents of the women in Tijuana are something special," Luther said. "I'm impressed you've helped these women by showing them a way to use their talents to earn money and contribute to their community."

Melissa took Luther's words to heart. She was happy to see how the community had thrived. Residents who'd previously been downtrodden by the pressures of poverty could now stand on their own. They were using their skills and talents to make money for themselves and for their church and could now care for themselves, their children, and their elderly relatives spiritually, emotionally, and physically.

***

Even though it was early on a Saturday morning, the dusty street corner was already buzzing in preparation for the children's event that the mission church of Cristo Redentor Lutheran Church was sponsoring that day. Preteen girls blew up balloons while keeping an eye out for their younger siblings. Men strung up pinatas. Other volunteers carefully wrote each family's name on the wrapped packages of rice, beans, and new socks and underwear that had been donated by LWML women and trucked down by Orphan Grain Train.

Mothers sat off to the side as children started to arrive and were funneled into one of the first activities: coloring tables. Even older children in Tijuana think coloring is a treat, as leisure time is at a premium and many families don't have the resources to purchase their own crayons.

"Niños! Let's gather together for our story time!" Melissa called out as she motioned for the children to sit on a large vinyl banner that had been Concordia's Easter sign that year and was now spread across the dirt yard.

"I am going to read to you out of this special book called the Bible. How many of you know what the Bible is?"

Only two children raised their hands.

"It is the Word of God," one child said.

"How many of you have ever read the Bible?" The children looked confused, and no one raised their hands this time.

"Let's read in the book of Matthew, chapter 19, where Jesus blessed the children. One day some parents brought their children to Jesus so he could lay his hands on them and pray for them. But the disciples—these were Jesus' friends—scolded the parents for bothering him. But Jesus said, 'Let the children come to me. Don't stop them! For the kingdom of heaven belongs to those who are like these children.' And he placed his hands on their heads and blessed them."

"Did you know that Jesus loved being with people? Did you know that he especially loved being with children? Why do you think that is?"

"Because he knows children love him," a little girl said.

"Good answer, amiga," Melissa said.

She looked over at the moms and saw that Tere had engaged them in a discussion over a parenting booklet they'd received when they'd arrived. Tere knew they might have trouble reading the booklet, so she had offered to visit them in their homes to answer any questions.

Melissa turned back to the children and continued. "Do you know Jesus loves us because he made us? He made you," she said, motioning to one of the children. "And you," she said as she motioned to one of the moms. The children enthusiastically nodded.

"Do you know Jesus loves people who are sitting in jail?" The children's eyes opened wide in disbelief. "Jesus loves all the people he made. He doesn't love the wrong things we do. Those things are called sins. They are things that we do or think that go against the best life that Jesus wants for us. But God knew that we couldn't make a way out of our sin alone, so he sent Jesus to die on a cross and pay for the sins of all the world. His sacrifice opened up heaven so that we could be with him forever! Isn't that amazing?"

"Oh, yes," the children nodded again.

"Not only that, but we have a job to do here on earth—to live and love like Jesus. It doesn't matter how young or old we are. You might think you are too little and you can't do anything important. But Jesus sent us a helper. We call him the Holy Spirit. And he provides the strength and power we need to do the things Jesus wants us to do."

The children were still paying close attention as Melissa asked them a set of 20 questions about the story of Jesus. They answered all of them correctly! Melissa prayed this information would stay tucked deep into their little hearts forever.

Then Melissa noticed a five-year-old girl humming to herself and bobbing her head.

"What is your name, little one, and what are you so happy about?" Melissa asked.

"I am happy because I know that Jesus loves me and my family and opened heaven for us and he wants me to be his helper too," she said.

"What do you want to help Jesus do, amiga?" Melissa asked.

"I want to help others love him!" she said, beaming. "My heart is so happy."

Melissa's heart was happy too. She had seen how people along the border had sacrificed and suffered to make a new life for themselves, much like her ancestors had sacrificed and suffered in order to make a new life for themselves in the United States. And despite setbacks and challenges, she'd focused on the people she'd vowed to serve.

But Melissa Salomón will never consider her mission fulfilled. She will always work to improve the lives of those who suffer and those in need. Her unique calling is to be an encourager, a bridge-builder, and a collaborator who reflects the ways of Jesus. And everyone who has been the benefactor of Melissa's kindness knows how much of a blessing to the world she truly is. Like her ancestors before her, Melissa has tenaciously tended to her flock of sheep with the love and compassion of a shepherd.

"Suppose one of you has a hundred sheep and loses one of them. Doesn't he leave the ninety-nine in the open country and go after the lost sheep until he finds it? And when he finds it, he joyfully puts it on his shoulders and goes home. Then he calls his friends and neighbors together and says, 'Rejoice with me; I have found my lost sheep'" (Luke 15:4-6).

** Many names and situations in this biography have been changed in an effort to protect the anonymity of some of the subjects

Epilogue

The COVID-19 pandemic drastically impacted the outreach abilities of One Thousand Generations. For many months Melissa was unable to go to Tijuana and spend time with the people of the community. But Tere, her husband, Sadoc, and their three sons, along with many other volunteers, continued to serve in Tijuana. One Thousand Generations functioned as an aid society during many months when people could not find work because of the shutdown. Here are a few examples of people One Thousand Generations helped during this difficult and unprecedented time.

Cuquita is a 76-year-old grandmother with a fractured hip who has been bedridden for twelve years. Her children don't adequately support her, and her attempts at rehabilitation have failed. She has fourteen children; she doesn't know where seven are. Some are drug addicts. Two of her daughters watch over her, but it was difficult to care for her properly during the COVID crisis. Tere called Cuquita daily, prayed with her, and read her passages from the Bible. Tere was a pivotal part of caring for Cuquita's spiritual health during this time.

Carlos is the young son of a bricklayer. His father used to earn a good wage, but during the pandemic work was scarce, as were the materials he needed. One Thousand Generations provided support to his family by giving Carlos a backpack full of spiritual materials in addition to food.

Memo, Ana, and Angel are the children of a single mother. Their mother drives a bus in order to make ends meet. While their mother works, their grandmother cares for them. One Thousand Generations offers a breakfast program that these children attend and supports this family's spiritual needs by giving them catechism materials.

Doña Mary is an ill grandmother and mother whose forty-two-year-old son suffers from epileptic seizures. Due to the pandemic and the limits on medical supplies in Mexico, the medicines Doña Mary needed for her illnesses and her son's seizures were not available. Doña Mary has a daughter in the United States who is suffering from cancer. Because of her poor health and pandemic travel restrictions, Doña Mary could no longer cross the border to take her daughter to the doctor. She sold clothing in the open market, but she didn't make enough to take care of her basic needs. The medical dispensary funded and supported by One Thousand Generations made sure Doña Mary had the medication she required.

Young Ramón Alejandro received his last chemotherapy treatment after nearly three years. Because of his illness he lived in quarantine prior to the pandemic, unable to see family and friends. Ramón had to follow a certain diet to keep him as healthy as possible, but it was expensive, and his family had trouble affording the specialized food. Despite his challenges, Ramón's faith remains strong. Once, after a treatment, Ramón experienced severe facial paralysis. After much prayer, his condition went away. Doctors could not explain what had happened, but Ramón was convinced prayer and his faith cured him. Today, he is an inspiration to those around him and shares his faith with others.

Cynthia and Eva are nursing students who need to complete three hundred hours of work to get their nursing licenses. They work with the One Thousand Generations medical dispensary, assisting with its elder care program. After discovering that several of the elders in the community were using canes because of poor foot and toenail care, Cynthia and Eva now offer therapeutic pedicures to those in the community who need it. They give about ten pedicures each day in addition to providing health checkups to about thirty residents. Their work with One Thousand Generations has taught them that care is more than just taking temperatures and even doing pedicures. It involves listening, compassion, and prayer.

These are just a few examples of the people One Thousand Generations has served. None would have been able to live such a productive life if it weren't for the persistence and love of Melissa Salomón, a tenacious missionary.

PARTIAL FAMILY TREE FROM MELISSA'S BRANCH OF THE GARCÍA FAMILY

Dear Garcia Family:

I have been doing some research on the Garcia family line and thought you all would like to know about the male Garcia line. There are two principal Garcia family lines in New Mexico: Garcia de Noriega who came to New Mexico in 1601 and Garcia de la Mora who came to New Mexico in 1733 from La Villa de Pozuelo de Almagro, Toledo, Spain. Our primary line is Garcia de la Mora, but we intermarried with the Garcia's de Noriega in 1793 and again in 1881.

Juan Garcia de la Mora   Manuela Gonzales

Born and stayed in Spain

Juan Pedro Garcia de la Mora   Maria Josefa Martin
                                                 Serrano
b. 1705 in Spain   b. 1718 in NM

Married 1733 – La Joya, San Juan Parish, NM

Antonio Garcia de la Mora   Josefa Griego
b. 1734, San Juan Parish

Francisco Garcia de la Mora   Maria Concepcion Garcia
b. 1775, Santa Fe Parish   de Noriega
                                                 b. 1775

Married 1793 – La Castrense

Felix Garcia de la Mora   Maria Francisca Romero
b. 1806, Santa Fe Parish   b. 1810

Married 1827 – La Castrense

Juan Manuel Garcia de la Mora   Maria Gregoria Velarde
b. 1834, Santa Fe Parish   b. 1835

Married 1855 – La Joya, San Juan Parish, NM

Elias Nepomuceno Garcia   Rebecca Garcia de Noriega
b. 1858, Abiquiu Parish   b. 1867, Coyote, Abiquiu
                                                 Parish

Married 1881

WANT TO READ MORE BIOGRAPHIES IN THE "MAKING OF A MISSIONARY" SERIES?

Mission Nation Publishing exists to "strengthen the church in America by giving a voice to the new missionaries to America." Please keep us in your prayers! Proceeds from sale of books goes to publish the next biography.

Robert Scudieri
President, Mission Nation Publishing

To order any of our books go to the Mission Nation Publishing website, www.MissionNationPublishing.org and look under "Books." Purchases of 25 books or more receive a discount. Interested? Email MissionPublisher@aol.com.

Other Books in the Making of A Missionary Book Series

THE DESPICABLE MISSIONARY The biography of "Victoria" (not her real name). Victoria grew up in Pakistan as a Christian girl. As a child she was mercilessly teased because she and her family were Christian. As she grew up, Victoria experienced discrimination in school and employment. She had grown to hate Muslims. Gradually, as her faith deepened, she realized Jesus' will for His followers was to love all people, even those that we see as enemies. This is a true story of a real person's growing to love her enemy. This could happen because of divine intervention. The book is for anyone seeking to become more forgiving. A study guide is available for this book.

NO ACCIDENTAL MISSIONARY Dr. Tesfai Tesema grew up in Ethiopia estranged from his parents' Christian faith. When a communist government came to power Tesfai joined the government. After a falling out, he was put in prison. Then, one day, he was "mistakenly" released. After a harrowing escape from Ethiopia, he made his way to Saudi Arabia. This is a true story of how, in Saudi Arabia, Christ found Tesfai and miraculously turned his life around. Today he is a missionary in America. This is a great lesson for anyone wondering if there is forgiveness for past errors.

THE BULLETPROOF MISSIONARY Prof. Shang Ik Moon was a child in North Korea during WW II. After the war, he had a harrowing escape to South Korea. When the Korean War began he lost his whole family and was reduced to finding food on garbage dumps and sleeping on the ground in a makeshift tent. Then an army chaplain took him under his care and helped him immigrate to the United States. He became the provost of a university and helped begin more than sixty Korean churches in the United States. How could this happen? Only by divine intervention. Everyone has a purpose, in those most far away from Christ. The book will encourage those who are looking for their purpose. A study guide is available for this book.

THE RESILIENT MISSIONARY Dr. Yohannes Mengsteab was a communist soldier, until he was wounded and escaped to the Sudan. There, Swedish Lutheran missionaries evangelized him. By God's intervention his life was turned around and he became an evangelist in the refugee camp. Today he is a mission executive for the Texas District of the Lutheran Church Missouri Synod., starting churches in America.

THE UNEXPECTED MISSIONARY The true story of Gagan Gurung. His family forced to leave Bhutan, he spent more than twenty years in a refugee camp in Nepal. He hid in Hindu temple rather than be baptized, but a miracle brought him to faith, and to America where he has baptized more than forty Nepalese refugees.

THE TENACIOUS MISSIONARY The biography of Melissa Salomon. Melissa grew up in the mountains of New Mexico where only Spanish was spoken. She learned English after a move to Los

Angeles when she was in grade school. Scholarships for "the little Spanish girl" got Melissa through college and law school. Frustrated by the inability of law to change the hearts and lives of the poor, she found her purpose in life when God opened a door for her to become a missionary to America.

THE APOSTOLIC CHURCH Where did the term "apostolic church" come from, and what is its full definition? There were Greek apostles and Jewish apostles during Jesus' time. Jesus did not invent the office of the apostle, but He did change it in one very important way. That is what the book is about.

THE MISSION BIBLE COMMENTARY SERIES The only mission commentary of the Bible in English. Written in simple English for all reading levels and meant particularly for those who speak English as a second language. Dr. Paul Bruns, a Bible translator in Africa developed this for emerging lay leaders. Available now: Romans, Luke-Acts, Hebrews-James.

Made in United States
Troutdale, OR
11/23/2024

25215041R00089